Contents

C000021262

About higher-order thinking skills

Teachers report that their curricula are lacking in materials that help pupils learn to think critically. This book provides practice applying higher-order thinking skills in English, maths, science, humanities and social sciences contexts.

What are higher-order thinking skills?

They are not the skills—such as alphabetising or calculating a perimeter—used in specific academic subjects. Rather, they are skills used across all curriculum areas and in non-academic situations; the skills for making use of information.

In this book, higher-order thinking skills are represented by behavioural verbs. Each page focuses on one behavioural verb, which is defined at the top of the page. Each behavioural verb is emphasised in the instructions so pupils become aware of when and how they are using the thinking skill.

Why is it important to practise higher-order thinking skills?

Teachers may debate which is the most important curriculum area or skill in school, but some things are widely accepted by teachers and academics alike:

- Pupils need well-developed thinking skills to be successful in the classroom, during assessments and in the real world.
- Pupils can learn to think better if they're taught how to do so.
- Critical thinking skills are more important than ever in today's competitive, rapidly changing, technology-based environment.

Young children naturally use thinking skills. They learn autonomy through exploration, observe their environment using logic and reasoning, try new things and think creatively. As children grow and enter an academic setting, some of their natural curiosity and problem-solving instincts are not engaged as often as they could be.

While all thinking skills are important, pupils generally get ample practice with recall, recognition, identification and comprehension. Therefore, this book focuses on thinking skills that are more challenging to incorporate. These include analysing, predicting, modelling, composing, organising, evaluating options, designing, critiquing and problem-solving.

People with strong critical thinking skills can accomplish a great deal, whether or not they have background knowledge in a topic. Critical thinkers know how to acquire new knowledge and how to approach problem-solving. They also know how to persevere and use productive struggle to find an answer.

Ten tips for tackling tough tasks

Before beginning these lessons, read the paragraph below to pupils, then share the tip that best supports each daily activity.

These activities are not supposed to be things you've already learned how to do in class. These activities let you exercise your brain in new ways. Most of the activities don't have just one right answer, so don't worry; just answer in a way that makes sense to you.

1 **Unpack the task:** Read the activity once to see what it's about. Then re-read it very carefully. Ask yourself: What am I being asked to do? Solve a problem? Complete a puzzle? Write a story? Explain my thinking? Describe something? Then look at the information given.

2 **Put yourself in the situation:** Spend a few minutes imagining that you are in the situation described. How does it feel? Why is it important? Is this situation like one you have been in before?

3 **Look for details:** If an activity has a picture or a map, look at it closely. Look at everything, work out what people are doing, and read any words. Think about which details might be the most important for what you have to do.

4 **Think about what you already know:** You already know a lot! If you're not sure how to begin, think about the topic or the objects you see on the page. Think about when you've seen or used something. Think about when you learned or talked about something.

5 **Think about what the activity is like:** Sometimes when you learn to do one thing, you can do the same thing in a similar situation. Ask yourself: Have I done something like this before?

6 **Share ideas:** If you can work with a partner or a group, talk about your ideas or where you are getting stuck. Sometimes different people have different parts of the answer. When you tell what you know, you can all succeed.

7 **Use trial and error:** If you can't get started, write down anything. Then compare it to what the activity asks for. Does it make sense or follow the activity's instructions? If not, why not? Then start to change your answer, little by little, so it does follow the instructions.

8 **Work backwards:** Sometimes it makes sense to start at the end. Work out where you want to end up. Then think about what your problem looks like just before that. What needs to happen to get from there to the end?

9 **Check your answers as you go:** After you write or draw your answer, re-read the question you are answering or the directions you are following. Does your response answer the question? Does it make sense? Does it follow the rules given? Does it solve the problem? If not, work out what part could be better and fix it.

10 **Keep trying:** Sometimes it takes a while for a new idea to come. Don't give up if you can't do an activity right away. When you work it out, you'll feel great!

HIGHER-ORDER THINKING SKILLS

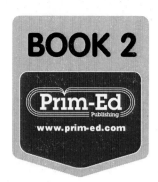

BOOK 2

Prim-Ed
Publishing
www.prim-ed.com

Over 100 Cross-curricular Activities to Build your Pupils' Critical Thinking Skills!

'what if' questions

picture comparisons

wordplay

logic and visual puzzles

creative writing

spatial brainteasers

Higher-order Thinking Skills – Book 2

Published by Prim-Ed Publishing 2020
Under licence from Evan-Moor® Educational Publishers

Copyright© 2018 Evan-Moor® Educational Publishers
This version copyright© Prim-Ed Publishing 2020

PR–8455

ISBN: 978-1-84654-987-8

Titles in this series:
Higher-order Thinking Skills – (Year 1/1st Class)
Higher-order Thinking Skills – (Year 2/2nd Class)
Higher-order Thinking Skills – (Year 3/3rd Class)
Higher-order Thinking Skills – (Year 4/4th Class)
Higher-order Thinking Skills – (Year 5/5th Class)
Higher-order Thinking Skills – (Year 6/6th Class)

Internet websites
In some cases, websites or specific URLs may be recommended. While these are checked and rechecked at the time of publication, the publisher has no control over any subsequent changes which may be made to webpages. It is *strongly* recommended that the class teacher checks *all* URLs before allowing pupils to access them.

View all pages online

Website: www.prim-ed.com

Email: sales@prim-ed.com

What's inside?

A variety of challenges

Curriculum-area contexts

Each full-page activity gives pupils an opportunity to practise a higher-order thinking skill in the context of a different curriculum area, rotating between English, mathematics, science, humanities and social sciences, and sometimes combining them with art or logic. Engaging formats include:

- logic and visual puzzles
- spatial brainteasers
- creative writing
- picture comparisons
- wordplay
- 'what if' questions

A behavioural verb representing a higher-order thinking skill is defined at the top of the page and highlighted in the directions. Topic information is often provided on the page so that the pupil can go past recall and comprehension to focus on using the given higher-order thinking skill.

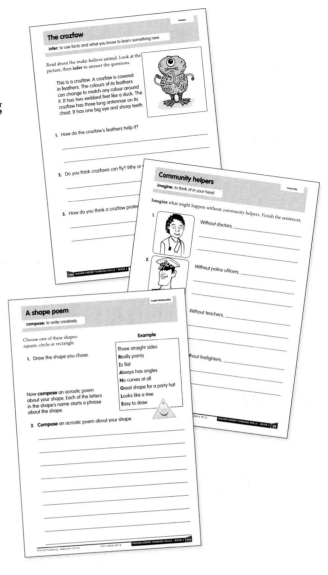

Behavioural verb definitions

The chart on pages xii and xiii lists the definition of each behavioural verb in the book. You may wish to reproduce these pages and distribute them to pupils.

Answers

Evaluate pupils' responses based on your own expectations and on what content pupils have encountered. Accept any reasonable response. Answers for the closed questions start on page 152.

How to use this book

1 Reproduce the activities or distribute a pupil book to each pupil. The activities are organised to become more challenging as the year progresses.

2 Introduce the daily activity to the whole class, reading the definition provided and relating it to any recent work done in class.

3 Review the directions and any information given to ensure pupils know what to do. It is recommended that pupils work with a partner or in a small group, although the activities do not require collaboration and may be completed independently by a capable pupil.

4 Many activities have multiple solutions or are open-ended. Allow sufficient time for sharing responses and discussing problem-solving approaches. Modelling a variety of ideas and strategies offers valuable learning benefits and encourages peer respect and cooperation.

Teaching tips

- Preview the page yourself before assigning it to the class. Most pages do not rely on specific prior academic knowledge, but you may wish to connect the activity to a prior classroom experience or lesson.

- Remind pupils that there are usually several ways to complete the activities, so they should not worry about finding 'the right answer'.

- Become familiar with the ten tips for tackling tough tasks on page iv. When you introduce each activity page, review with pupils any tip(s) that you think might be particularly useful for them on that particular task.

- Pupils may take some time to work out how to start; productive struggle is often part of the higher-order thinking process. If they are getting frustrated and the ten tips aren't helping, guide pupils with leading questions.

- Take the opportunity to call to their attention any behavioural verbs used in other academic lessons to reinforce pupils' understanding and awareness of when they are using these skills.

Higher-order thinking categories

Behavioural verb	Page number	Page title	Cross-curricular link
analyse	9	Home sweet home	Science
	13	Button patterns	Mathematics
	67	What's the connection?	English
	118	Meal deal	Mathematics
apply	23	A super chart	Mathematics
	113	Time for ice cream!	Mathematics
arrange	16	New plants	Geography/Science
	55	All about Brandon	History
	58	Stack the apples	Mathematics
assemble	17	Putting it all together	English
	92	Making words	English
categorise	14	Setting things in motion	Science
	24	Common needs	Science
	54	What's in a habitat?	Science
	60	Something in common	Geography/Science
	72	Things in common	English/Mathematics
choose	30	Trip to the library	History/Geography/Citizenship
compare	37	Alike and special	English
	46	The shape of water	Geography/Science
	52	Different places	English
	69	Same needs, different solutions	Science
	74	Home sweet home	Science
	80	Looking at the world	Geography
	83	Find the dinosaur eggs	Mathematics
	100	Old school, new school	History
compile	71	Teddy bears for sale	Mathematics/English
compose	66	Holiday notes	Science/English
	111	A shape poem	English/Mathematics
convince	129	I don't believe you!	Science
create	110	A trip to the museum	Geography/History/Citizenship
	148	Out of this world	Art/Mathematics

Higher-order thinking categories

Higher-order thinking categories

Behavioural verb	Page number	Page title	Cross-curricular link
evaluate	87	The best pet	English/Science
	106	Habitats for people	Science/Geography
	114	Animal coverings	Science
examine	4	Studying our world	Science
	49	Mystery objects	Science
	95	Name that feature!	Geography
	125	Look closely!	Geography
expand	103	Growing shapes	Mathematics
explain	31	Tool for every room	English
	88	Busy bee	Mathematics
	105	In the suburbs	Geography
form	53	Juggling fun	Mathematics
generate	90	Give directions!	Mathematics
give an example	7	Show me!	English
	29	Heat it, freeze it, mix it	Science
	44	Be sensible	Science
	99	A world of matter	Science
hypothesise	19	Naming places	History/Geography
	104	Helpful body parts	Science
	115	Community helpers	Citizenship
	150	What do you think?	History
illustrate	2	Many homes	English
imagine	57	Mousing around	English
	65	Community helpers	Citizenship
	147	Someone else for a day	English

Higher-order thinking categories

Behavioural verb	Page number	Page title	Cross-curricular link
infer	6	Dress for the season	Geography/Science
	70	Who said it?	English
	78	Hocus, pocus!	Mathematics
	102	What is it?	English
	117	What's going on?	English
	124	The crozfaw	Science
	135	The longest route	Geography
interview	42	Getting to know you	English
	81	What's your life like?	English/Citizenship
	107	Tell me about yourself!	English
invent	26	Memory sentence	Mathematics/English
justify	39	Knock, knock, who's there?	Science
	75	On the farm	Science/Geography
	127	Be an editor!	English
	146	Which car is best?	English
order	21	Don't be late!	English/Mathematics
	38	Farmer Joe's animals	Mathematics
	61	A busy morning	English/Mathematics
	121	Up, up and away!	Geography/Mathematics
organise	98	Row, row, row	Mathematics
	123	Clever counting	Mathematics
persuade	141	Going shopping!	Mathematics
plan	8	Forgetful Ernie	Mathematics
	15	Road trip!	Geography
	33	The bugs' ball	Mathematics
	48	On target	Mathematics
	93	Addition challenge	Mathematics
predict	18	Coin patterns	Mathematics
	32	What will happen next?	English
	64	Plant predictions	Science
	86	What's next?	English
	144	What's for dinner?	Science
prepare	136	It's a party!	English
prioritise	94	Party planning	Science/English

Higher-order thinking categories

Behavioural verb	Page number	Page title	Cross-curricular link
propose	140	Funfair fun	Health and Physical Education
prove	132	Prove it!	English
	143	A crawling race	Mathematics
rank	101	Favourite activities	English
	119	Cool it!	Science
rearrange	28	Add 'em up!	Mathematics
recommend	10	Rules, rules, rules!	Health and Physical Education
represent	25	My year in school	History
	84	Snow tracking	Mathematics
	112	Swimming with details	English
revise	56	Building the future	English
rewrite	22	Hiding synonyms	English
	35	Wrong direction	Mathematics/Geography
	142	Where's the haiku?	English
sequence	77	Gone fishing	English
solve	82	Riddle me this	English
	130	Toy shopping	Mathematics
	139	Broken window	Science/Design and Technology
sort	5	Name it!	Citizenship
	12	What kind of thing?	Mathematics/Science
	62	List mix-up	English
state the rule	68	Race car numbers	Mathematics
suggest	34	Too hot!	Science
	41	Reusing things	English
	85	What are the rules?	Health and Physical Education
	137	Helpful ideas	English/Citizenship
support	20	In the city	Geography
	122	Making music	English
	134	The better idea	English/Citizenship
visualise	27	What do you see?	English
	45	Musical zoo pens	Mathematics
	133	Sharing stickers	Mathematics
work out	149	That's not a fish!	Science

Behavioural verb definitions

analyse: to study how parts go together

apply: to use what you know in a new way

arrange: to put in the best place

assemble: to put parts together

categorise: to name a group

choose: to decide what is best

compare: to look for things that are the same or different

compile: to gather facts together

compose: to write creatively

convince: to make someone agree with you

create: to make something new

critique: to tell what is good and bad about something

decide: to choose after thinking

deduce: to use facts to work something out

describe: to tell how something looks, sounds, smells or feels

design: to plan how something will look

determine: to work out

display: to arrange and show

distinguish: to tell the difference between things

eliminate: to take out something that does not belong

estimate: to give an idea about the size or value of something

evaluate: to judge carefully

examine: to look at closely

expand: to make something bigger

explain: to give good reasons for your thoughts or for what you did

form: to bring parts together to make something

generate: to make something

give an example: to show one thing in a group

hypothesise: to make a good guess based on reasons

illustrate: to represent in a picture

 978-1-84654-987-8 www.prim-ed.com Prim-Ed Publishing

Behavioural verb definitions

imagine: to think of in your head

infer: to use facts and what you know to learn something new

interview: to ask someone questions about his or her life

invent: to create for the first time

justify: to give a good reason for something

order: to list things in a certain way

organise: to make something easy to understand or do

persuade: to make someone want to do something

plan: to find a good way to do something

predict: to tell what will probably happen

prepare: to get ready for something

prioritise: to work out what is most important

propose: to suggest an idea or a solution

prove: to show that something is true or false

rank: to put in order by value

rearrange: to put things in a better order

recommend: to tell the best ideas

represent: to show in a drawing or a graph or with a symbol

revise: to improve something by changing it

rewrite: to change something by writing it again

sequence: to put things in the order they happen

solve: to find an answer to a problem

sort: to put things into groups

state the rule: to tell the way something is done

suggest: to tell an idea

support: to explain a choice

visualise: to imagine how something will look

work out: to find an answer

Many homes

illustrate: to represent in a picture

Pretend that an author asked you to help **illustrate** her story.
Read the story. Underline the part that is already illustrated.

Mika was a neighbourhood cat. He didn't have one home. He had many homes. Some days he stayed with a family who lived in a house. He slept with the little boy who lived there. The bed was so cosy and warm.

Other days, Mika visited a grandmother who fed him delicious food from a can.

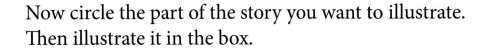

At other times, he played with a puppy that lived in an apartment. Mika was a happy cat.

Now circle the part of the story you want to illustrate.
Then illustrate it in the box.

Fishy maths

determine: to work out

Read the clues to **determine** how many fish are in each tank. Draw them and write the matching addition sentence. The first one has been started for you.

1. There are 9 fish in all. There is 1 more fish in Tank A than in Tank B.

   _____ + _____ = _____

Tank A   **Tank B**

2. There are 10 fish in all. There are 2 fewer fish in Tank A than in Tank B.

   _____ + _____ = _____

Tank A   **Tank B**

3. There are 12 fish in all. There are 2 more fish in Tank A than in Tank B.

   _____ + _____ = _____

Tank A   **Tank B**

4. There are 11 fish in all. There are 3 fewer fish in Tank A than in Tank B.

   _____ + _____ = _____

Tank A   **Tank B**

Studying our world

examine: to look at closely

Scientists study the world around us. **Examine** each picture. Write what kind of scientist each person is and explain what you think he or she does.

1.

_____ scientist

_____

_____

_____

2.

_____ scientist

_____

_____

_____

3.

_____ scientist

_____

_____

_____

Name it!

sort: to put things into groups

Look at the pictures.

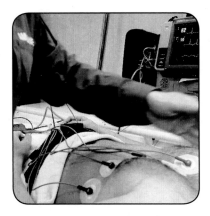

paramedic

police car

firefighter

police officer

fire engine

ambulance

Sort the pictures into two groups. Write the name of each group, then write the names of the pictures under the group they belong in.

Group 1: _____

Group 2: _____

1.

2.

Dress for the season

infer: to use facts and what you know to learn something new

Look at the pictures of the seasons and the clothes people wear.
Draw a line to match.

1.

| winter | spring | summer | autumn |

Infer and write why people wear those clothes in each season.

2. winter: _____

3. spring: _____

4. summer: _____

5. autumn: _____

Show me!

give an example: to show one thing in a group

A child from another country does not know what the underlined words mean. Draw or write to **give an example** of what each word means.

1. a <u>hot</u> thing	**2.** a <u>wet</u> thing
3. a <u>quiet</u> thing	**4.** a <u>loud</u> thing
5. a <u>sticky</u> thing	**6.** a <u>sharp</u> thing

Forgetful Ernie

plan: to find a good way to do something

Ernie wrote some equations, but he forgot the + and – signs! **Plan** which signs can go in the circles to make the equations true. Write the signs.

1. 5 ◯ 3 ◯ 2 = 6

2. 8 ◯ 4 ◯ 1 = 5

3. 7 ◯ 2 ◯ 2 = 3

4. 3 ◯ 9 ◯ 2 = 14

Ernie tried again. This time he remembered the signs but forgot the numbers! **Plan** which numbers can go in the circles to make the equations true. Write the numbers.

5. ◯ – ◯ – ◯ = ◯

6. ◯ + ◯ + ◯ = ◯

7. ◯ – ◯ + ◯ = ◯

8. ◯ + ◯ – ◯ = ◯

 978-1-84654-987-8

Home sweet home

analyse: to study how parts go together

Analyse the pictures, then complete the questions.

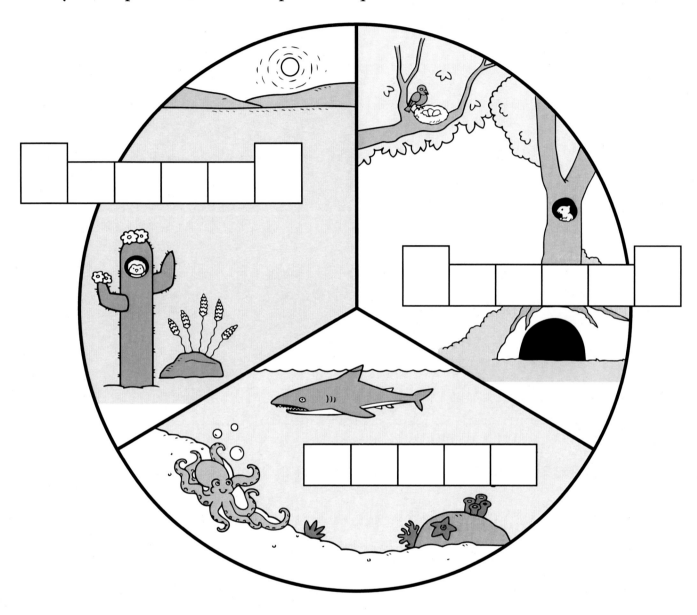

1. What is the same about all three of these pictures?

   _____

   _____

2. Each picture is missing its label. Work out what the missing labels are and write them in the boxes.

Rules, rules, rules!

recommend: to tell the best ideas

Look at the picture.

1. **Recommend** four rules for the playground. Draw a ✓ in four boxes.

    ☐ Play well with others.   ☐ Stay inside the fence.

    ☐ Run very fast.   ☐ Yell very loudly.

    ☐ Use the playground safely.   ☐ Listen to the teacher.

2. Why are these rules the best?

    _____

    _____

Feathered friends

deduce: to use facts to work something out

Chirpy, Pip and Tuck each live in a different tree. Read the clues to **deduce** what kind of tree each bird lives in. As you read each clue, fill in the chart, then answer the questions.

- Chirpy does not live in the elm tree.

- Pip does not live in the oak tree.

- Tuck does not live in the pine tree.

- The bird who lives in the oak tree has the longest name.

	elm	oak	pine
Chirpy	✗		
Pip			
Tuck			

1. Who lives in the oak tree? _____

2. Who lives in the elm tree? _____

3. Who lives in the pine tree? _____

What kind of thing?

sort: to put things into groups

Look at the pictures of the items. Look at the group name on top of each box. **Sort** each of the items into a group and draw each item in the correct box.

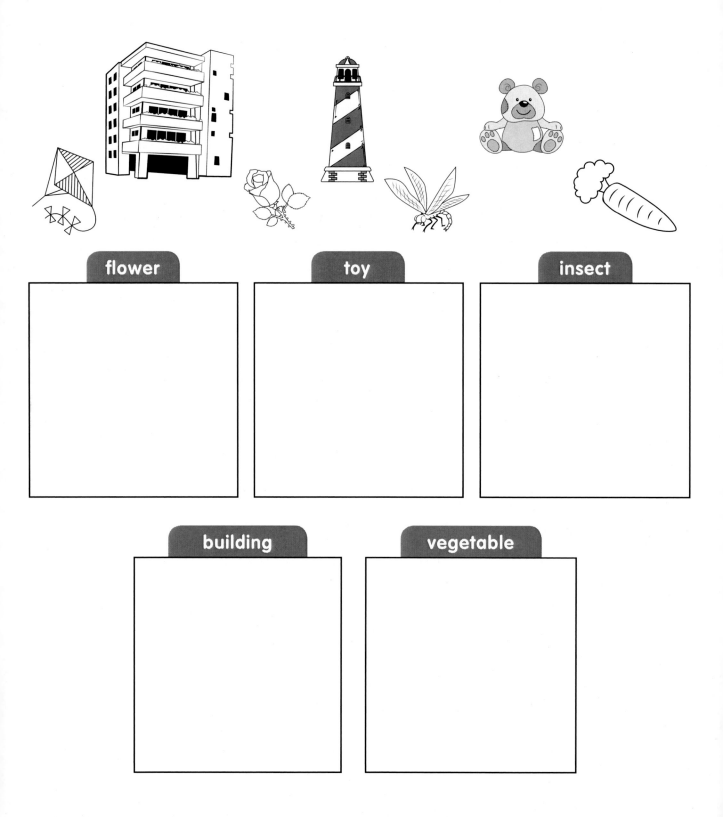

flower	toy	insect

building	vegetable

Button patterns

analyse: to study how parts go together

Yuna is making patterns with buttons.
Analyse the button patterns and complete the items.

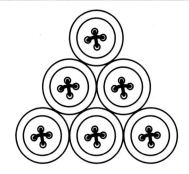

1. Look at each row. How did each
   row change from the row above it?

   _____

   _____

2. Look at the three shapes Yuna made.

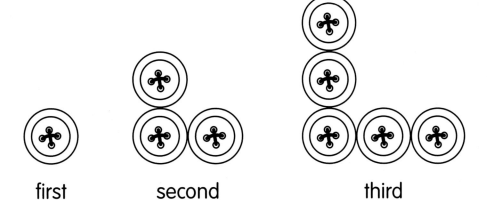

   first   second   third

   How did the number of buttons in each shape change?

   _____

3. Describe how the shape changed.

   _____

   _____

Setting things in motion

categorise: to name a group

Look at the pictures.

carrot	cart	rope
doorbell	shoe	pram
door	wagon	drawer

Coby put the pictures into groups. Think about how he grouped them. Finish the sentence to **categorise** the groups in the chart.

Group 1	Group 2	Group 3
1. cart	1. carrot	1. door
2. pram	2. rope	2. shoe
3. doorbell	3. wagon	3. drawer
Group 1 has objects that move with a _____.	Group 2 has objects that move with a _____.	Group 3 has objects that move with a _____.

Road trip!

plan: to find a good way to do something

Joy wants to take a road trip through the many towns and states of Australia. **Plan** her route.

Draw an X on the map on every town Joy wants to see. Then draw a line from her home in Melbourne through the states and back home again.

Joy wants to see these towns/cities:

Newcastle	Alice Springs	Adelaide
Mount Isa	Kalgoorlie	Cairns

1.

2. Which states will Joy drive through?

_____

_____

_____

New plants

arrange: to put in the best place

Help Dilip **arrange** his new plants in his garden. Read about each plant, then look at Dilip's garden. Write the name of each plant in the spot where it will grow best in his garden.

wood fern
Needs shade and lots of water.
Mist on hot days.

ivy
Grows to 10 m in sunshine. Will climb up or sideways.

lemon tree
Likes sunshine and damp soil.

Putting it all together

assemble: to put parts together

Put the letters together to **assemble** words. Write each word.

1. e d b   _____

2. s i m w   _____

3. o k b o   _____

4. y p l a   _____

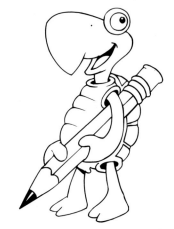

Put the words together to **assemble** sentences.

5. grass farm the eat horses the on

   _____

6. smiled he baby when me the saw

   _____

7. my wonder boots I are where

   _____

8. the camels you show watch about should

   _____

Coin patterns

predict: to tell what will probably happen

Jen and Ian got some coins from their piggy banks, then they each made a pattern with **10 coins**. Look at how their patterns start. **Predict** which pattern will have the greater value with all 10 coins, then write or draw to check your prediction.

Jen's pattern started like this:

(20) (5) (20) (5) (20) (5)

Ian's pattern started like this:

(20) (10) (5) (20) (10) (5)

My prediction

1. I predict that _____'s pattern has the greater value

   because _____

   _____.

Checking my prediction

2. Jen: _____

   _____

3. Ian: _____

   _____

4. I found out that _____

   _____.

Naming places

hypothesise: to make a good guess based on reasons

Look at the pictures. How do you think the places got their names?
Hypothesise why and how the towns got their names.

1. This town was named Alice Springs

because _____

_____

_____.

2.

This town was named Broken Hill

because _____

_____.

In the city

support: to explain a choice

Look at the picture. Find the things that do not belong. Circle them.

Write a reason to **support** why each thing does not belong.

1. _____

   _____

2. _____

   _____

3. _____

   _____

Don't be late!

order: to list things in a certain way

Look at the map of a neighbourhood. If all the children leave for school at the same time, who will arrive first? Who will arrive last?

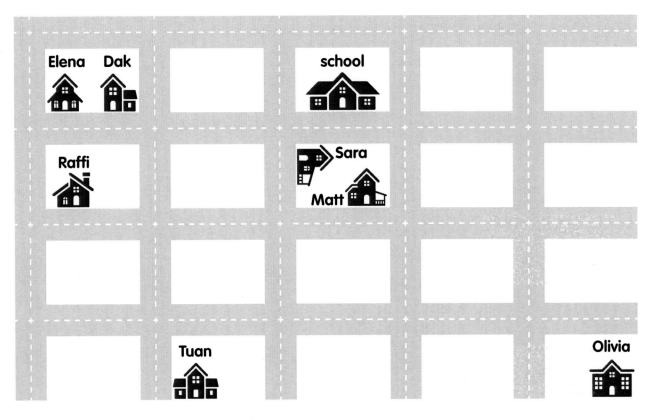

Order the children's names from who will arrive first to who will arrive last.

1. _____

2. _____

3. _____

4. _____

5. _____

6. _____

7. _____

8. Eric is moving to the neighbourhood. He will live the same distance from the school as Tuan but on a different block. Draw on the map where Eric's home could be.

Hiding synonyms

rewrite: to change something by writing it again

Synonyms are words that mean the same thing. Think of a synonym that can be used to **rewrite** the underlined word in each sentence and write it on the line. Then find and circle the synonym in the word search puzzle. If you can't find the synonym you wrote, try a different synonym.

1. Alma is <u>sick</u> today.   _____

2. <u>Start</u> on page 12.   _____

3. He's <u>scared</u> of the dark.   _____

4. We are <u>happy</u> that you came.   _____

5. They moved into a new <u>house</u>.   _____

r	i	q	h	o	m	e	k
o	l	u	t	b	h	r	a
m	l	a	d	a	i	w	f
o	u	v	o	s	g	o	r
n	b	e	w	c	d	l	a
d	k	z	h	y	i	r	i
b	e	g	i	n	k	s	d
i	g	l	a	d	g	h	y

A super chart

apply: to use what you know in a new way

Use the hundred chart
to add and subtract.

To solve 31 + 42, find 31
on the chart. Count down
four rows to add 40. You get
71. Then count over two spaces
to add 2. You get 73.

Hundred chart

1	2	3	4	5	6	7	8	9	10
11	12	13	14	15	16	17	18	19	20
21	22	23	24	25	26	27	28	29	30
31	32	33	34	35	36	37	38	39	40
41	42	43	44	45	46	47	48	49	50
51	52	53	54	55	56	57	58	59	60
61	62	63	64	65	66	67	68	69	70
71	72	73	74	75	76	77	78	79	80
81	82	83	84	85	86	87	88	89	90
91	92	93	94	95	96	97	98	99	100

Apply the same steps as above
to solve each problem. Write how
you solve it.

1. Solve 45 + 24 starting with 24.

_____

_____

_____

2. Solve 76 – 25 starting with 76.

_____

_____

_____

Common needs

categorise: to name a group

Look at the pictures. **Categorise** the pictures to finish the sentence, then answer the question.

1.
   _____ need these things to live.

2.
   _____ need these things to live.

3.
   _____ need these things to live.

4. What do each of the answers above have in common?

_____

Look at the words in the crossword puzzle.
Write an example of each word as a puzzle clue.

5. _____

6. _____

7. _____

	5			6		
	p	e	o	p	l	e
				l		
7						
a	n	i	m	a	l	s
				n		
				t		
				s		

My year in school

represent: to show in a drawing or a graph or with a symbol

Think about important events that happened last year at school.

1. Draw important events that **represent** what you did during these months last year.

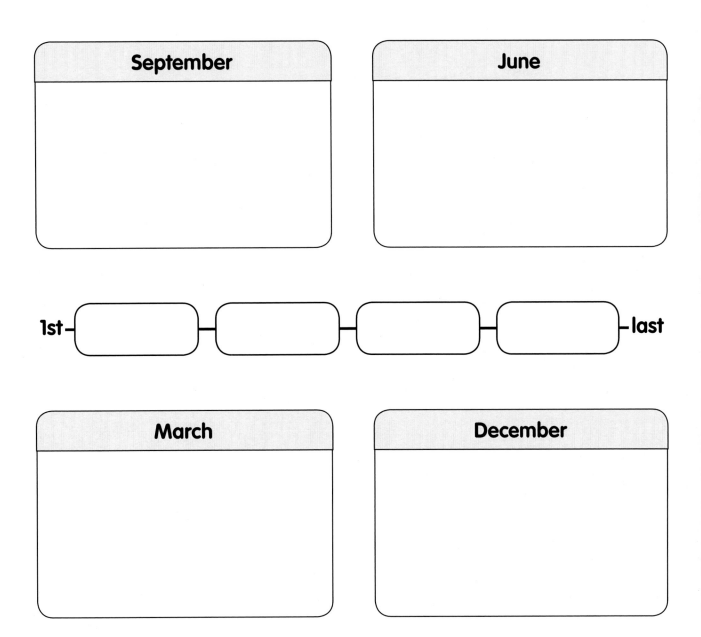

2. Draw a line from each picture to the timeline in order from first to last. Write the month on the timeline.

Memory sentence

invent: to create for the first time

Read, then complete the activity.

Most months of the year have 30 or 31 days.

Days in each month

January	31	February	28 or 29	March	31
April	30	May	31	June	30
July	31	August	31	September	30
October	31	November	30	December	31

Do you have trouble remembering how many days are in each month? Here's a way to remember.

Use a short memory sentence. Each word in the sentence starts with the same letter as the word you want to remember. For example, you could say 'Fresh apple juice sounds nice' to remember that February, April, June, September and November are the shorter months.

Now **invent** your own memory sentence to remember which months have 31 days.

J_____ m_____ m_____ j_____

a_____ o_____ d_____

What do you see?

visualise: to imagine how something will look

Read the poem and **visualise** what it is describing, then circle the picture that looks most like what you pictured in your mind.

1. Covered in little black spots
   It lands on my arm

Now read this poem and **visualise** what it is describing.

2. Reaching to the sky
   More windows than I can count
   I feel small beneath

   Draw what you pictured in your mind.

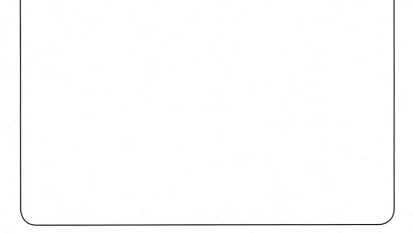

   What did you **visualise**?

   _____

Add 'em up!

rearrange: to put things in a better order

Buster needs to add all these numbers together.
He adds the numbers one after the other.

4   5   7   8   3   6

1. Think of a way to **rearrange** the numbers so that they are easier to add. Show your way in the box.

2. Explain why the way you rearranged the numbers makes it easier to find the sum. Remember to include the sum.

_____

_____

_____

_____

Heat it, freeze it, mix it

give an example: to show one thing in a group

Read, then complete the items.

Some things change when you heat them. Some things change when you freeze them. Some things change when you mix them. Write what causes the things below to change: heating, freezing or mixing.

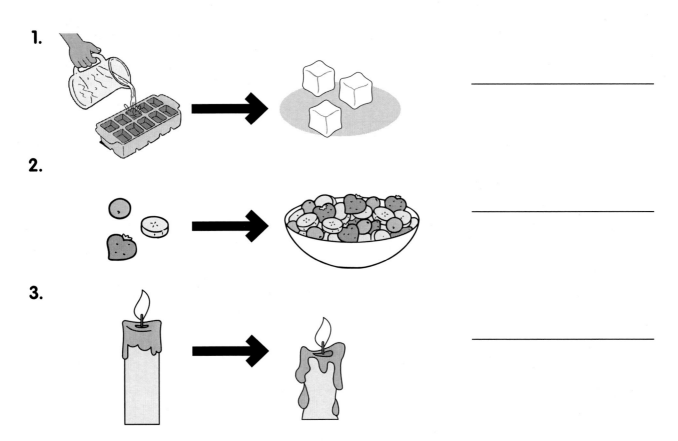

1. _____

2. _____

3. _____

Give an example of sweet treats you can make by heating, freezing and mixing.

4. If I heat _____, I can make _____.

5. If I freeze _____, I can make _____.

6. If I mix _____ and _____, I can make _____.

Trip to the library

choose: to decide what is best

Read the questions. **Choose** the part of the library where you could find the answer and draw a line.

1. What is the post office used for?

2. Who was Ned Kelly?

3. Where is South America?

4. Why was Elvis Presley famous?

5. Why are hospitals open during the day and night?

6. What is a landmark?

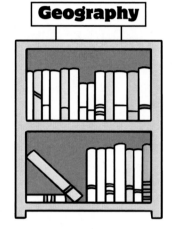

Tool for every room

explain: to give good reasons for your thoughts or for what you did

Draw a line from the tool to the place you use it, then **explain** your answers.

1.

   | bathroom | | classroom | | kitchen |

2. I use the [pencil] in _____ to

_____ .

3. I use the [spoon] in _____ to

_____ .

4. I use the [toothbrush] in _____ to

_____ .

Draw one more tool you use. Write a sentence about it.

5.

_____

_____

_____

What will happen next?

predict: to tell what will probably happen

Look at the pictures, then **predict** what will happen. Circle the sentence with your prediction.

1.

The snowman will melt.

It will start to rain.

The snowman will find a friend.

2.

The car will stay where it is.

The car will go faster.

The car will turn around.

Predict what will happen next, then write about it.

3.

_____

_____

_____

4.

_____

_____

_____

The bugs' ball

plan: to find a good way to do something

Read and solve the problem.

Pretend some insects and spiders went to a fancy dance. Insects have six legs, and spiders have eight. If there were 40 dancing legs, how many insects and spiders were there?

1. **Plan** how you will solve the problem. Write or draw your ideas in the box.

2. There were _____ insects and _____ spiders at the dance.

Too hot!

suggest: to tell an idea

Read about Kalia's problem. **Suggest** two different things she can do. Draw pictures and write your ideas.

Kalia puts her hot chocolate on the table. It is too hot to drink, but Kalia doesn't want to wait.

1.

_____

_____

_____

_____

2.

_____

_____

_____

_____

Wrong direction

Mathematics/
Geography

rewrite: to change something by writing it again

Peter told Risa where the park was, but she is lost. **Rewrite** Peter's directions.

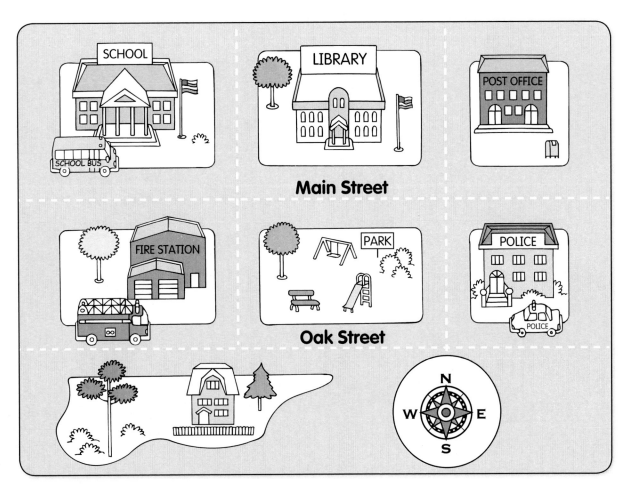

Peter's directions

The park is

N of the library

S of the post office

E of Oak Street

W of the school

Your directions

The park is

N of _____

S of _____

E of _____

W of _____

Your own playground

design: to plan how something will look

Look at the pictures. Circle four. Use them to **design** a map of a playground. Draw your map in the box.

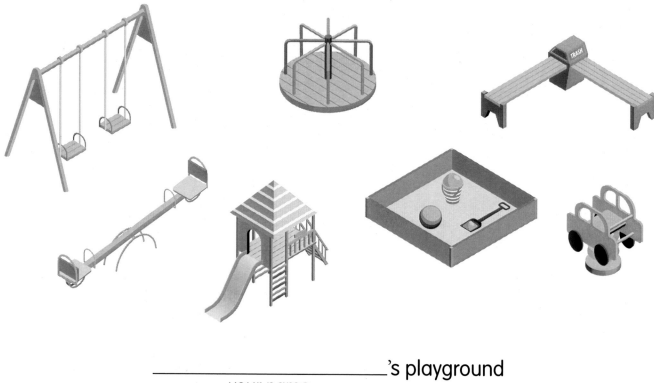

_____'s playground
your name

Alike and special

compare: to look for things that are the same or different

Compare a tiger and a dog. Complete the Venn diagram to show how they are alike and different. It has been started for you.

1.

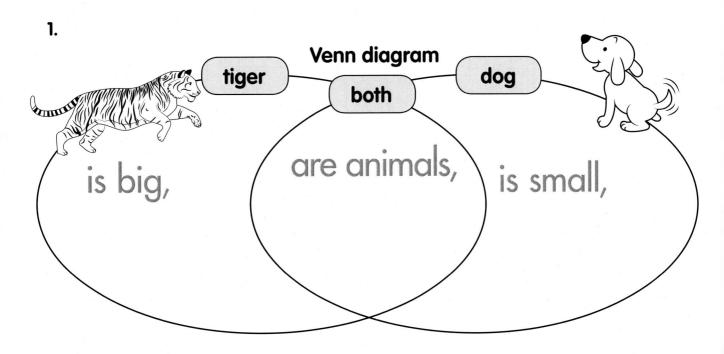

Venn diagram

tiger   both   dog

is big,   are animals,   is small,

Compare a bicycle and a van. Complete the Venn diagram.

2.

Venn diagram

bicycle   both   van

Farmer Joe's animals

order: to list things in a certain way

Farmer Joe's animals stand in a row. Read the clues to help you **order** where they are, then write the names of the animals on the correct lines.

🔍 Billy is between Flo and Ace.

🔍 Muffin is between Lucky and Ace.

🔍 Ace and Flo eat hay.

🔍 Lucky sleeps by Farmer Joe's bed at night.

1. _____ 2. _____ 3. _____ 4. _____ 5. _____

Knock, knock, who's there?

justify: to give a good reason for something

Look at the pictures. Who do you think lives in each of these animal homes? **Justify** your answers.

1.

I think _____ lives here

because _____

_____

_____.

2.

I think _____ lives here

because _____

_____

_____.

3.

I think _____ lives here

because _____

_____

_____.

Then and now

distinguish: to tell the difference between things

Look at the pictures. **Distinguish** between how the city looked in the past and how it looks today.

1. Label each picture with **past** or **today**.

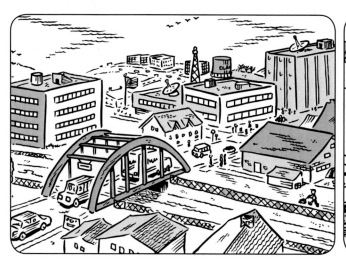 

_____   _____

2. Explain why you labelled each picture the way you did.

past: _____

_____

today: _____

_____

_____

Reusing things

suggest: to tell an idea

The pictures below show things we use every day. Write how each object is usually used, then **suggest** two other ways the object can be used.

1.

is used to: _____

other uses: _____

_____

2.

is used to: _____

other uses: _____

_____

3.

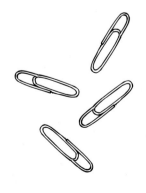

is used to: _____

other uses:_____

_____

4.

is used to: _____

other uses: _____

_____

Getting to know you

interview: to ask someone questions about his or her life

Look at the people. Draw a line matching each person with his or her job.

teacher   nurse   firefighter

Now choose a person you would like to **interview** about his or her job. Circle the picture, then write four questions you would like to ask that person.

1. _____

_____

2. _____

_____

3. _____

_____

4. _____

_____

Chunky chocolates

deduce: to use facts to work something out

Read the text and look at the pictures of the boxes.

At the Chunky Chocolate Factory, chocolates are sold in round boxes and square boxes. All the round boxes have the same number of chocolates. All the square boxes have the same number of chocolates.

+ = 22 chocolates

+ + = 34 chocolates

+ + = 32 chocolates

Deduce how many chocolates are in each kind of box.

1. There are _____ chocolates in the .

2. There are _____ chocolates in the .

Be sensible

give an example: to show one thing in a group

You use your senses to learn about things around you. Read the sentence about a sense, then draw to **give an example** of the sense. Write another sense you can use with the example you drew.

---

1. Draw something you can taste.

another sense: _____

2. Draw something you can smell.

another sense: _____

3. Draw something you can hear.

another sense: _____

4. Draw something you can feel.

another sense: _____

978-1-84654-987-8   www.prim-ed.com   Prim-Ed Publishing

Musical zoo pens

visualise: to imagine how something will look

All the animals are moving to different pens. **Visualise** where they will end up.

The zebras and the lions will trade places.
The bear will move one pen to the left.
The giraffes will move in with the elephants.
The elephants will move into the empty pen.

1. Which animals will be in the corner
    between Wild Way and Animal Path? _____

2. Which other animals will be near Animal Path? _____

The shape of water

compare: to look for things that are the same or different

Look at the pictures and **compare** them, then read and answer the questions.

This is a stream.

This is a lake.

Tani thinks that a lake and a stream are alike.
Hope thinks that they are different.

1. Do you agree with Tani, with Hope, or with both of them? Why?

   I agree with _____ because _____

   _____

   _____

   _____.

2. What is another body of water that is like a stream? _____

3. What is another body of water that is like a lake? _____

What is it?

describe: to tell how something looks, sounds, smells or feels

You and a friend are playing a guessing game. Your friend **describes** something without saying its name. You guess what it is.

1. It's very big. It has a long trunk and big, floppy ears.

   What is it? _____

Now it's your turn to **describe** things to your friend. Write three things about each object. Don't use the name of the object.

2. _____

3. _____

4. _____

5. _____

6. _____

7. _____

On target

plan: to find a good way to do something

Lucia shot three arrows. She scored 62 points.
Each arrow hit a different number on the target.
What numbers did the arrows land on?
Plan how you will solve the problem, then use
your plan to find the answer.

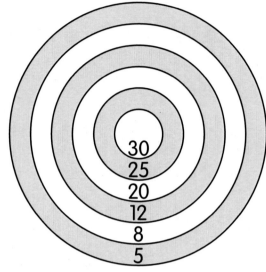

My plan

1. _____

   _____

   _____

My work

2.

3. The arrows landed on _____, _____, and _____.

Mystery objects

examine: to look at closely

Examine each shadow. Write what you think it is and why.

1.

This is the shadow of _____

because _____

_____.

2.

This is the shadow of _____

because _____

_____.

3.

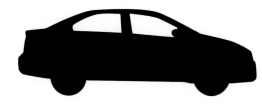

This is the shadow of _____

because _____

_____.

In the future

design: to plan how something will look

Look at the cars. **Design** a picture of what you think a car will look like in the future.

Past

Present

Future

Casey's clues

deduce: to use facts to work something out

Casey lives in an apartment building. Read Casey's clues to **deduce** where he lives. As you read each clue, cross off the apartments that are not his. When you have finished, the one that is left is Casey's.

There are no plants in Casey's window.

Casey's window has no curtains.

Casey does not live on the bottom floor.

The window above his does not have any plants.

Describe where Casey's apartment is.

_____

_____

Different places

compare: to look for things that are the same or different

Compare a restaurant and a shop. Complete the Venn diagram to show how they are alike and different.

1.

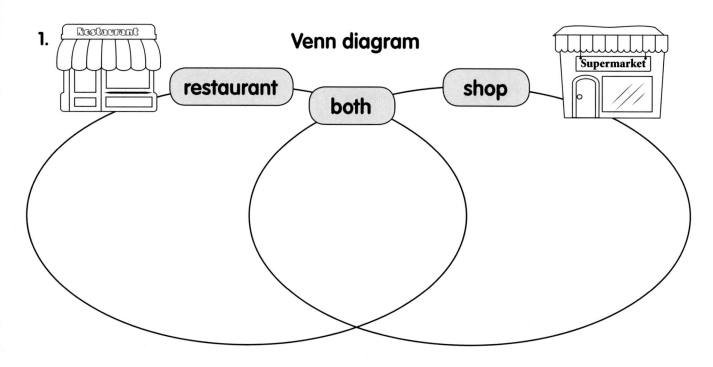

Now **compare** the Internet and TV. Complete the Venn diagram.

2.

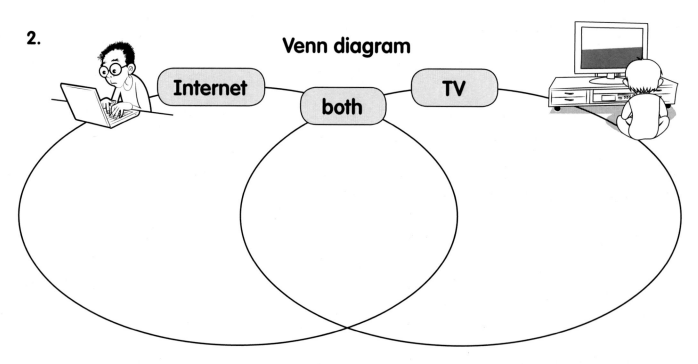

Juggling fun

form: to bring parts together to make something

Use the numbers on the balls to **form** three-digit numbers that match the clues.

1. the largest number _____

2. the smallest number _____

3. the largest number with 8 in the

   tens place _____

4. the largest odd number that is

   less than 600 _____

5. the largest odd number _____

6. the smallest number with 3 in the

   ones place _____

7. the smallest number that is

   greater than 500 _____

8. the smallest even number _____

What's in a habitat?

categorise: to name a group

Look at this habitat. **Categorise** the things in this habitat into two groups.

1. **Group 1:**

   _____ _____ _____

   These things are in a group because

   _____ .

2. **Group 2:**

   _____ _____ _____

   These things are in a group because

   _____ .

 978-1-84654-987-8 www.prim-ed.com Prim-Ed Publishing

All about Brandon

arrange: to put in the best place

These pictures show Brandon at different ages. Draw a line from each picture to the timeline to **arrange** the pictures from youngest to oldest. Write Brandon's age in the circles. Then answer the question.

1. **age 70**

age 13

age 5

age 30

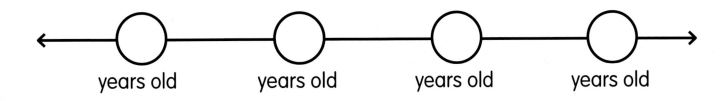

years old   years old   years old   years old

2. How did you know how to **arrange** the pictures?

_____

_____

Building the future

revise: to improve something by changing it

Read the paragraph and circle the opinions. **Revise** the paragraph so that it contains only facts, then rewrite the paragraph on the lines.

I want to be like Aunt Kemi when I grow up. She is really cool. She helped her dad build things when she was little. Her dad said she was really good at it. She decided to build houses for her job. Her father said that no one would hire a girl to build houses. That is such a stupid idea! Aunt Kemi went to a special class to learn more about it. She got an A. Then her teacher hired her! Her houses are the best ones in our town.

_____

_____

_____

_____

_____

_____

_____

Mousing around

imagine: to think of in your head

Imagine that you wake up one day and are the size of a mouse! What would the world around you look like?

Draw a picture of how the things in your bedroom would look.

1.

Imagine what life would be like and how you would feel.
Write three sentences.

2. _____

3. _____

4. _____

Stack the apples

arrange: to put in the best place

Pretend you work at a supermarket. You need to put ten apples in a triangle shape. The apples are red, yellow and green. No apple can touch another apple of the same colour. Show how you can **arrange** the apples below. Colour them red, yellow or green.

1. Write how many you have of each apple.

red _____   yellow _____   green _____

2. Is there more than one way to **arrange** the apples? _____

   Explain your answer. _____

   _____

   _____

Lift off!

deduce: to use facts to work something out

Read the clues about something in space.
Deduce what it is and finish the sentence.

1. I am a ball of hot gas. I look like a tiny dot of light.
   People like to make a wish when they see me.

   I am a ___ ___ ___ ___.
       4   3

2. I do not make my own light. I travel around Earth.
   I am big and round.

   I am a ___ ___ ___ ___.
       1

3. We travel around the sun.
   There are eight of us.
   We all spin around.

   We are ___ ___ ___ ___ ___ ___ ___.
      5   7

4. I have seven continents.
   I have five oceans.
   I am home to people and animals.

   I am planet ___ ___ ___ ___ ___.
          6   2

Write the numbered letters to finish the sentence.

5. The rocket flies to ___ u ___ e ___ ___ ___ ___ c ___.
              1   2   3   4   5   6   7

Something in common

categorise: to name a group

Look at the pictures. **Categorise** them into three groups, then write what is in each group.

 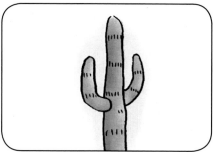 

1. Group 1:

2. Group 2:

3. Group 3:

_____   _____   _____

A busy morning

order: to list things in a certain way

Read the list of small jobs Mrs Brown has to do, then look at the map. In which order should she do her jobs? Put a number next to each job on the list to **order** them.

Jobs

1. Buy chicken and carrots. _____

2. Take her son to school. _____

3. Buy stamps. _____

4. Return library books. _____

5. Take Mr Lee some soup. _____

6. Buy food for the fish. _____

7. Buy a hammer. _____

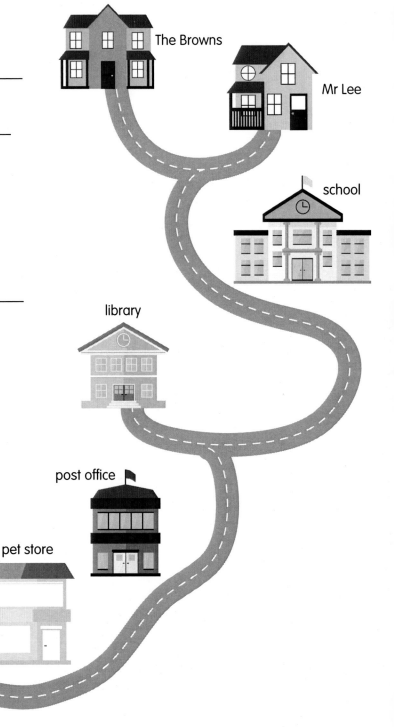

List mix-up

sort: to put things into groups

Mr Edo's weekly spelling lists have words on the same topic. Amy's spelling cards from three lists have got mixed up. Look at the spelling cards to work out the topics of the spelling lists. Write the topics on the lists, then draw lines to **sort** the cards.

Spelling lists

1.

topic:
_____
1.
2.
3.
4.

2.

topic:
_____
1.
2.
3.
4.

3.

topic:
_____
1.
2.
3.
4.

Spelling cards

monkey

spanner

pasta

hammer

owl

pizza

lion

snake

screwdriver

hamburger

cake

saw

Mystery numbers

deduce: to use facts to work something out

A magician wrote three numbers on a piece of paper, then he put the paper in his hat. **Deduce** which numbers he wrote. Read the clues to help you work out the mystery numbers.

- The numbers are between 300 and 350.

- The numbers are odd and are three digits long.

- The sum of the three digits in each number is even.

- The tens digit is greater than the ones digit.

Work space

What are the numbers? _____ _____ _____

Plant predictions

predict: to tell what will probably happen

Read the text, then **predict** what will happen next.

1. The chimp eats an apple. An apple seed drops to the ground. It starts to rain.

   What will happen to the seed?

   _____

   _____

   _____

2. Tran plants a seed in the soil.
   Tran never waters the seed.

   What will happen to the seed?

   _____

   _____

   _____

3. Megan plants a plum tree in her garden.
   The tree makes flowers in the spring.
   She sees bees around the tree.

   What will happen to the tree?

   _____

   _____

   _____

Community helpers

imagine: to think of in your head

Imagine what might happen without community helpers. Finish the sentences.

1.  Without doctors, _____

   _____

   _____.

2.  Without police officers, _____

   _____

   _____.

3.  Without teachers, _____

   _____

   _____.

4.  Without firefighters, _____

   _____

   _____.

Holiday notes

compose: to write creatively

Read the text, then complete the items.

1. Mrs Dutta has a lot of plants. She is going to visit her sister for two weeks. Mrs Dutta will hire a plantsitter to take care of her plants. Help her **compose** a note to tell the plantsitter what to do.

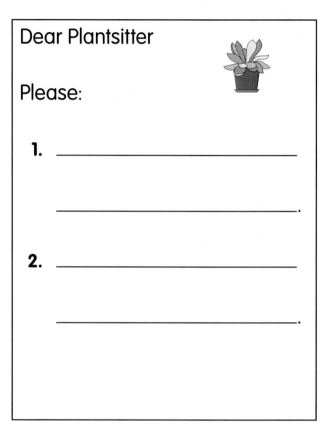

Dear Plantsitter

Please:

1. _____

   _____.

2. _____

   _____.

2. Mrs Dutta also has a dog, named Flopsy. She will hire a dogsitter to take care of Flopsy. Help her **compose** a note to tell the dogsitter what to do.

Dear Dogsitter

Please:

1. _____

   _____.

2. _____

   _____.

What's the connection?

analyse: to study how parts go together

Analyse the objects on the first pair of puzzle pieces. How are the cow and milk connected? Now look at the object on the second pair. Which object below has the same kind of connection with it? Circle it.

Example:

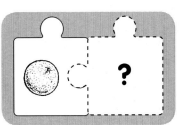

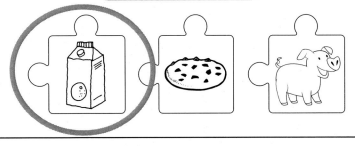

1.

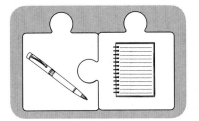
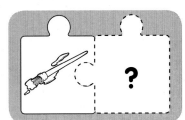

2.

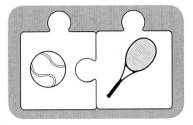
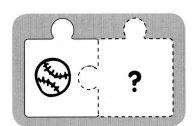

Race car numbers

state the rule: to tell the way something is done

Study the number patterns on the race cars. Write the missing numbers, then **state the rule** for each pattern.

1.

What's the rule? _____

2.

What's the rule? _____

3.

What's the rule? _____

4.

What's the rule? _____

Same needs, different solutions

compare: to look for things that are the same or different

Animals and people are living things. They both have the same basic needs. They meet their needs in different ways.

Look at the pictures. Finish the sentences to **compare** how the boy and the bear meet their needs.

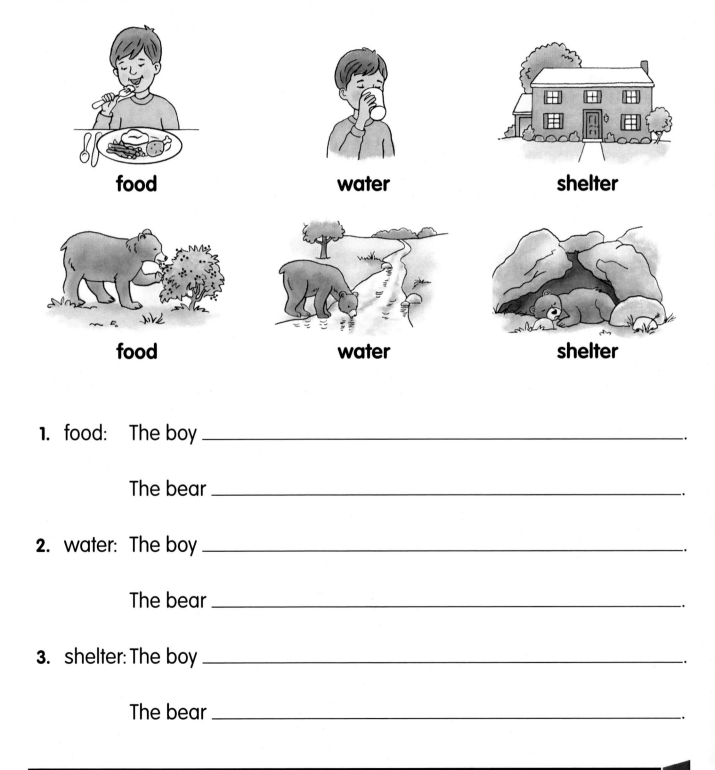

food   water   shelter

food   water   shelter

1. food: The boy _____.

   The bear _____.

2. water: The boy _____.

   The bear _____.

3. shelter: The boy _____.

   The bear _____.

Who said it?

infer: to use facts and what you know to learn something new

Read the statements. **Infer** who would say each one, then write the letters next to the person.

A. 'I work in the office.'

B. 'I plan fun maths lessons.'

C. 'I help others read.'

D. 'I update the school website.'

E. 'I follow instructions.'

F. 'I help my friends.'

Pupil   Teacher   Secretary

Teddy bears for sale

compile: to gather facts together

A toy shop has only a few teddy bears left. They are brown, white or pink. Each one comes with a red, blue or yellow bow. **Compile** the information in an advertisement and list all the different teddy bears.

Things in common

categorise: to name a group

Look at the group. What do the things have in common? **Categorise** the things in the group.

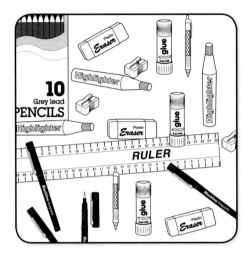

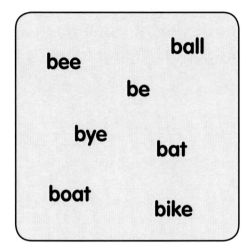

1. _____

_____

2. _____

_____

Now look at these things. Sort them into two groups, then circle the things in each group in a different colour.

Categorise each group.

3. _____

4. _____

Number line mice

estimate: to give an idea about the size or value of something

Estimate where each mouse is on the number line. Explain the reason for your estimate.

1.

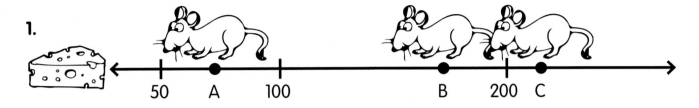

50   A   100   B   200   C

mouse A: _____ reason: _____

_____

mouse B: _____ reason: _____

_____

mouse C: _____ reason: _____

_____

2.

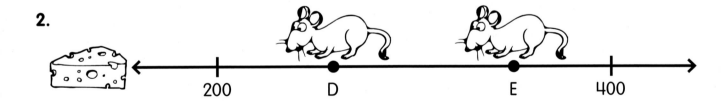

200   D   E   400

mouse D: _____ reason: _____

_____

mouse E: _____ reason: _____

_____

Home sweet home

compare: to look for things that are the same or different

Look at the pictures of habitats and **compare** them.

A forest habitat

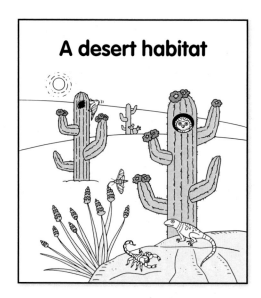

A desert habitat

Complete the Venn diagram to show how a forest and a desert are alike and different.

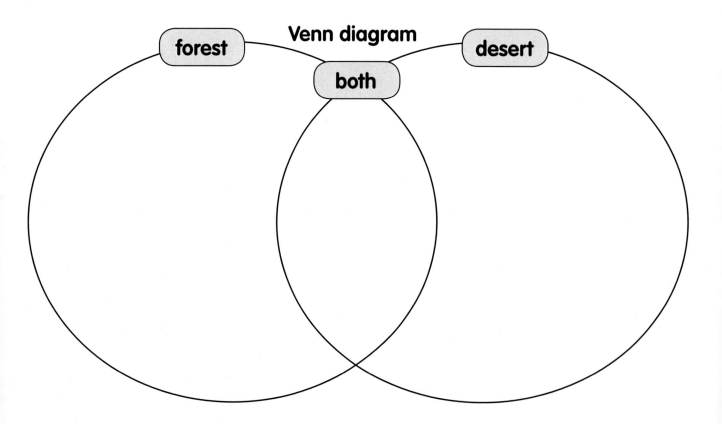

Venn diagram

forest   both   desert

On the farm

justify: to give a good reason for something

Look at the picture. Circle the things that do not belong.

What did you circle? **Justify** why it does not belong.

1. _____

_____

2. _____

_____

3. _____

_____

Under the sea

display: to arrange and show

Look at this underwater scene. Complete the items.

1. Draw three other kinds of sea animals. Add at least one of each.

2. How many of each animal do you have? **Display** the answer on a graph.

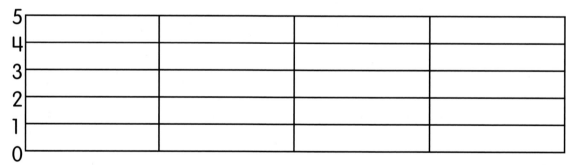

Kind of animal

3. How many sea animals are in your picture in total? _____

4. Write another question that can be answered with the graph.

_____

Gone fishing

sequence: to put things in the order they happen

Read the story. Its paragraphs are mixed up. **Sequence** them to make the story clear, then write the number of each paragraph on the line.

Joey and the fish

_____ He noticed fish swimming in the creek. He had an idea.

_____ Joey put the fishing line in the creek. No fish bit the hook. Then he put some bread from his sandwich on the hook. The bread kept falling off.

_____ It was really hot last summer. Joey went to the creek every day. He stuck his feet in the cool water.

_____ Then he saw a worm crawling in the grass. Joey put the worm on the hook. It worked! Joey was so happy to catch a fish! But now what? He put the fish back in the water.

_____ The next day, Joey came to the creek with a fishing pole. He really wanted to catch a fish in the creek, but he wasn't sure how.

Hocus, pocus!

infer: to use facts and what you know to learn something new

Oh, no! A fun-loving wizard has made some numbers disappear from the problems below!

Look at each addition and subtraction problem. **Infer** which numbers are missing, then write them in the boxes.

1.

```
    2   3   □
+   1   5   2
─────────────
    3   □   6
```

2.

```
    4   1   2
+   □   6   3
─────────────
    6   □   5
```

3.

```
    □   4   3
+   4   1   5
─────────────
    9   □   8
```

4.

```
    5   8   3
−   4   □   1
─────────────
    □   2   2
```

5.

```
    □   6   9
−   7   □   3
─────────────
    1   0   6
```

6.

```
    4   □   5
−   2   3   □
─────────────
    2   4   5
```

7.

```
    1   7   6
+   5   □   2
─────────────
    7   1   □
```

8.

```
    6   □   3
+   2   8   3
─────────────
    □   0   6
```

9.

```
    7   4   □
−   □   7   4
─────────────
    3   7   5
```

Amazing materials

determine: to work out

Help Reese walk to the pet shop. **Determine** which objects are made from wood. Circle them, then draw a line to connect them.

1.

Finish the sentence.

2. All the things that magnets attract are made of _____.

Looking at the world

compare: to look for things that are the same or different

Compare the map and globe, then answer the questions.

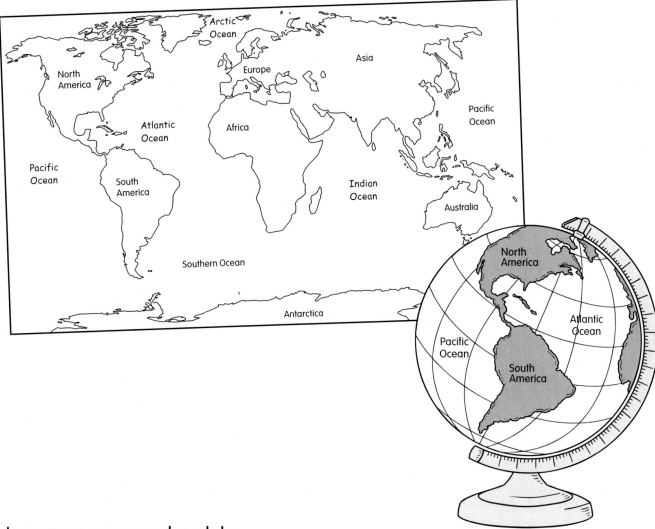

How are a map and a globe …

the same?   **different?**

1. _____   4. _____

2. _____   5. _____

3. _____   6. _____

What's your life like?

interview: to ask someone questions about his or her life

Look at the photos and the globe. Choose who you would like to **interview** about their life and country. Circle the picture.

 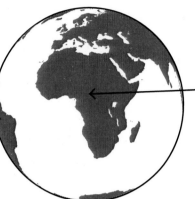 

Luis and Enzo are nine.
They live in Brazil.

Abal is eight.
She lives in Ghana.

Write four questions for your interview.

1. _____

_____

2. _____

_____

3. _____

_____

4. _____

_____

Riddle me this

solve: to find an answer to a problem

First work out the secret code. Here are four words written in the code.

words:	one	two	three	four
in code:	eno	owt	eerht	ruof

1. What is the secret to the code?

_____

Now use the same code. Decode the answers to **solve** the riddle.

2. Riddle: What are the four days that start with the letter 'T'?

     yadseuT   yadsruhT   yadot   worromot

Use the code to write two secret messages of your own.

3. message: _____

   in code: _____

4. message: _____

   in code: _____

Find the dinosaur eggs

compare: to look for things that are the same or different

Each dinosaur has laid a set of three eggs. Read each dinosaur's clue. **Compare** the numbers in each set of eggs, then match them to a dinosaur.

1.

The numbers on my eggs go from largest to smallest.

Set _____

2.

The numbers on my eggs have 4 in the tens place.

Set _____

3.

All the numbers on my eggs are greater than 670.

Set _____

4.

All the numbers on my eggs

_____.

Set _____

The set that is left over belongs to the last dinosaur. Write the letter of the set, then write a clue to describe the set.

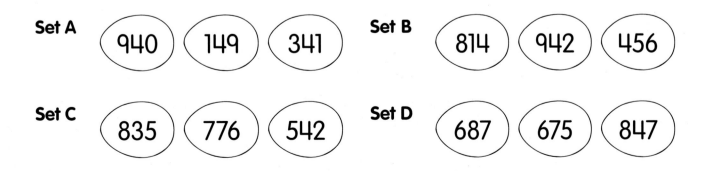

Set A   940   749   341

Set B   814   942   456

Set C   835   776   542

Set D   687   675   847

Snow tracking

represent: to show in a drawing or a graph or with a symbol

Mrs Lutz's class kept track of how much rain fell each week in March. Complete the items.

1. **Represent** the information on the graph.

Week 1: 5 cm   Week 3: 3 cm

Week 2: 8 cm   Week 4: 5 cm

Write two questions that can be answered using the graph, then answer them.

2. _____

3. _____

_____

What are the rules?

suggest: to tell an idea

Look at the picture.

Suggest three rules to help this classroom.

1. _____

   _____

2. _____

   _____

3. _____

   _____

What's next?

predict: to tell what will probably happen

Look at the picture. **Predict** what will happen next.

_____

_____

_____

The best pet

evaluate: to judge carefully

Which pet would be best for you? **Evaluate** what is good and bad about each pet. Think about where you live and the kind of care each pet needs.

	Good	Bad
1.		
2.		
3.		
4.		

5. What other animal might be a good pet for you?

_____

Why? _____

Busy bee

explain: to give good reasons for your thoughts or for what you did

The bee is in a hurry to get to the flower. It can only fly up ↑ or to the right → from dot to dot.

Draw lines on the grids to illustrate the different paths the bee can take. One path has been drawn for you.

Example

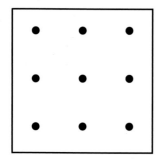

1.

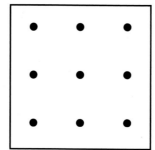

2.

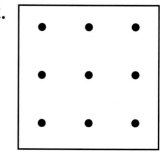

3.

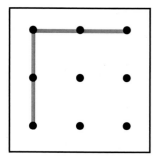

4.

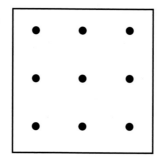

5.

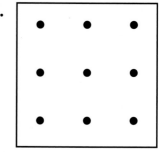

6. If you were the bee, which path would you take? **Explain** why.

_____

_____

_____

Another cycle

determine: to work out

Help Nikky get to Granny's house. **Determine** which items can be recycled. Circle them, then draw a line to connect the things you circled to get to Granny's.

1.

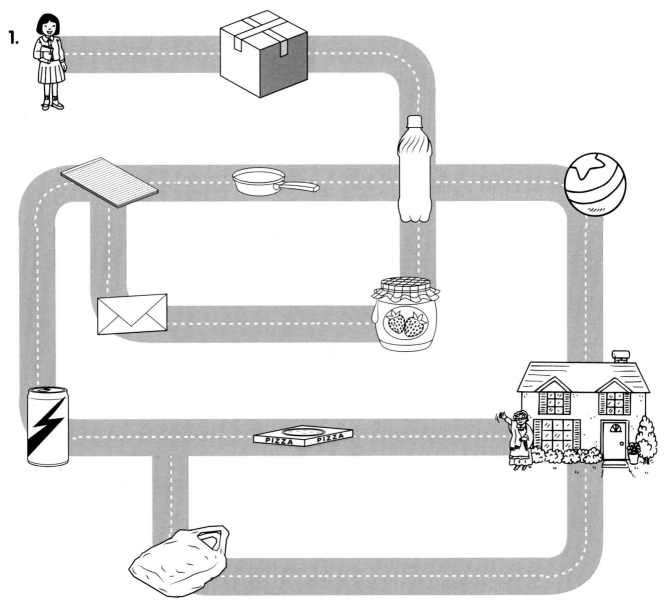

Finish the sentences.

2. Some materials can be _____.

These include a_____, p_____, g_____ and

certain p_____.

Give directions!

generate: to make something

Doug can't find his mum at Wild World Park. He is at the log ride. His mum is on the phone and gives him directions to meet her at the gift shop.

Generate, or write, the directions Doug's mum gives him using north, south, east and west.

_____

_____

_____

_____

Fact or opinion?

eliminate: to take out something that does not belong

Read Haru's paper. **Eliminate** (cross out) a sentence if it is an opinion.

	Facts about Steve Irwin
	Steve Irwin was a popular zookeeper and crocodile hunter.
	He was awesome.
	Even though he died, his family still runs Australia Zoo.
	I would love their job!

How did you decide which sentences to **eliminate**?

_____

_____

Making words

assemble: to put parts together

It can be fun to make, or **assemble**, a new word by putting two words together. For example, look at these words. One is a real word, and one is a new, made-up word:

sun + shine = sunshine   camp + drop = campdrop

Use the words in the word box to **assemble** two real words and two new, made-up words. Then draw or write what you think each word means.

arm	bow	bed	cat	cup	den	farm	ground
line	moon	pit	rain	rise	room	tea	yard

Real words	**New, made-up words**
1. _____	3. _____
2. _____	4. _____

Addition challenge

plan: to find a good way to do something

Fill in the boxes.

1. Think of two 3-digit numbers that add up to 500. Write them in the boxes.

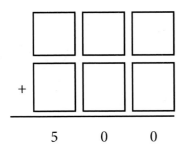

2. Now write two more numbers that add up to 500 without using any digit more than once.

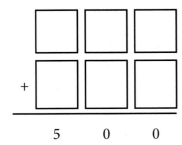

Explain how you **planned** your answer to the second problem.

3. _____

_____

_____

_____

_____

Party planning

prioritise: to work out what is most important

Blake's dad has a lot to pick up for Blake's birthday party. Think about the order he should do the things on his list.

1. Write the numbers 1, 2, 3, 4 and 5 to **prioritise** the order Blake's dad should do things.

To-do list

- ☐ buy ice
- ☐ buy party hats
- ☐ pick up ice cream cake
- ☐ pick up balloons
- ☐ buy crisps and soft drinks

2. What did you choose for number 4? Explain why.

_____

_____

3. What did you choose for number 5? Explain why.

_____

_____

Name that feature!

examine: to look at closely

Examine the close-up pictures of Earth's features. Write the name below the picture, then answer the question.

1. It is _____.
How can you tell?

_____

2. It is _____.
How can you tell?

_____

3. It is _____.
How can you tell?

_____

4. It is _____.
How can you tell?

_____

Artistic shapes

design: to plan how something will look

You can use shapes to make interesting art.

Example

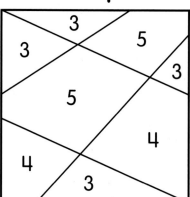

1. Draw several straight lines across the box to **design** interesting shapes. Count the number of sides each shape has. Write the number inside the shape. Then colour your 'artistic shapes' to make a bright picture.

2. Write how many of each shape you made.

   triangle (3 sides) _____   quadrilateral (4 sides) _____

   pentagon (5 sides) _____   hexagon (6 sides) _____

   other _____

Nouns everywhere

distinguish: to tell the difference between things

Read the text. Circle all the common nouns and proper nouns.

I go to Lincoln Primary School. It is very close by. I like
my new teacher, Mr Tucker. He is great. I really
love it when he reads stories like *Frog and Toad*.
He reads what the characters say in different voices.

Now **distinguish** between common nouns and proper nouns. List them.

1. common nouns

2. proper nouns

_____   _____

_____   _____

_____   _____

_____   _____

3. Look at both lists of nouns. Explain how you **distinguished** common nouns from proper nouns.

_____

_____

_____

_____

_____

Row, row, row

organise: make something easy to understand or do

A family is going rowing. They must follow these rules.

☑ The four family members will use two boats.

☑ Each boat will carry the same weight.

Organise who will ride together. Add the weights to make sure each total is the same, then write the names next to the boat.

Dad	Mum	Katie	Scamp
69 kg	61 kg	28 kg	20 kg

Work space

1. _____

2. _____

A world of matter

give an example: to show one thing in a group

Look at the pictures. Follow the directions.

1. Cross out the object that is not a solid.

Draw to **give an example** of one more solid. Also draw something else that is <u>not</u> a solid.

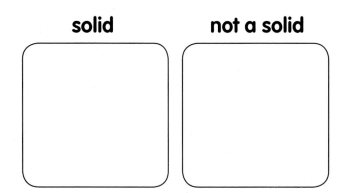

solid	not a solid

2. Explain what a solid is.

_____

3. Cross out the object that is not a liquid.

Draw to **give an example** of one more liquid. Also draw something else that is <u>not</u> a liquid.

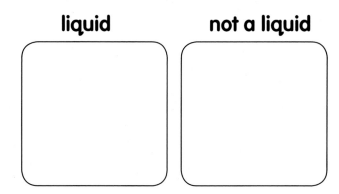

liquid	not a liquid

4. Explain what a liquid is.

_____

Old school, new school

compare: to look for things that are the same or different

Look at the picture from long ago and the picture from today. **Compare** the two pictures.

Long ago

Today

Write two things that are the same.

1. _____

2. _____

Write two things that are different.

3. _____

   _____

4. _____

   _____

Favourite activities

rank: to put in order by value

Look at these classes at the community centre. Think about which classes you would like to take.

1. **Rank** the classes from 1 to 6. Write 1 next to your favourite choice, 2 next to your second choice, and so on.

Community centre classes

Art _____

Karate _____

Basketball _____

Music _____

Dance _____

Swimming _____

Explain why you chose your first choice and your last choice.

2. first choice: _____

   _____

3. last choice: _____

   _____

What is it?

infer: to use facts and what you know to learn something new

Use the clues in the sentences to **infer** what the made-up, underlined word means. Draw a line to match.

1. Long ago, when <u>yekstibs</u> lived, there were no people.

2. I need a brown <u>reclew</u> to colour the tree trunk.

3. The <u>imnazes</u> are ripe! Let's pick some.

4. Where are my <u>dutus</u>? I can't see them.

5. All the animals feared the <u>pliman</u>.

6. Ricky is walking his <u>fofyfy</u>.

7. The teacher sharpened all the <u>ugvenes</u>.

Growing shapes

expand: to make something bigger

Yuna is making patterns with buttons. **Expand** the button patterns to make larger shapes. Answer the questions and draw the shapes.

1. Yuna wants to add three more rows. Each row will change the same way the rows above it changed. Draw three more rows.

    How many more buttons will she need?

    _____ more buttons

2. Yuna wants to add a fourth shape. It will change the same way the shapes before it changed. Draw the fourth shape.

    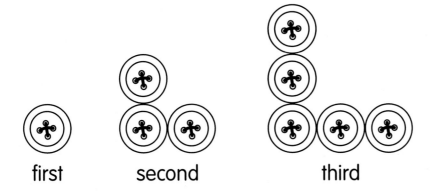

    first   second   third   fourth

    How many more buttons will she need?

    _____ more buttons

Helpful body parts

hypothesise: to make a good guess based on reasons

Read, then **hypothesise** to answer the questions.

Insects have body parts that help them do many things.
Insects have six **legs** that help them hop and walk. Most insects have **antennae** that help them smell, hear and feel their way around. Some insects have **wings** that help them fly.

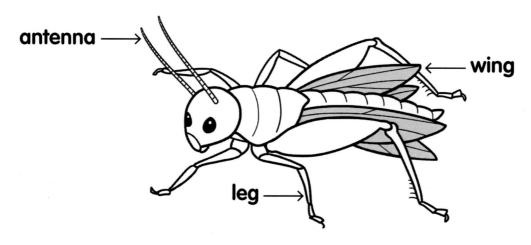

antenna ——→   ←—— **wing**

leg ——→

1. How do you think flying helps the insect?

   _____

   _____

2. What body parts are the antennae similar to on people?

   _____

3. What would happen if the insect did not have antennae?

   _____

   _____

In the suburbs

explain: to give good reasons for your thoughts or for what you did

Look at the picture. Circle the things that do not belong.

What did you circle? **Explain** why it does not belong.

1. _____

_____

_____

2. _____

_____

_____

Habitats for people

evaluate: to judge carefully

Pioneers had to travel to new lands and work out where to settle.
Pretend you are a pioneer and you come to each of these habitats.
Evaluate if it would be a good place to settle and state why/why not.

1.

Is it a good place to settle?

yes   **no**

_____

_____

2.

Is it a good place to settle?

yes   **no**

_____

_____

3.

Is it a good place to settle?

yes   **no**

_____

_____

4.

Is it a good place to settle?

yes   **no**

_____

_____

Tell me about yourself!

interview: to ask someone questions about his or her life

Think of a famous person you would like to **interview** and get to know better. Here are a few ideas.

1. Whom would you like to **interview**? _____

Write three questions you would ask him or her.

2. _____

   _____

3. _____

   _____

4. _____

   _____

2-D shape puzzler

determine: to work out

There are many 2-D shapes in the box.
Use the clues to **determine** what the shapes are. Draw the shapes in each box below. Write the names of the shapes.

1. The shape has four sides the same size.

   _____

2. The shape has four corners, two long sides and two short sides.

   _____

3. The shape has six sides the same size and six corners.

   _____

4. The shape has three corners and three sides. None of the sides are the same size.

   _____

5. Draw two more triangles.

What gives?

distinguish: to tell the difference between things

Ms Salib's class tested items in their classroom to see if they can be changed. Look at the results. Fill in the graph to show the results, then finish the sentences to **distinguish** the two groups of items.

item	easily changeable? yes	no
rock		
paper		
aluminium can		
nuts		
saucepan		

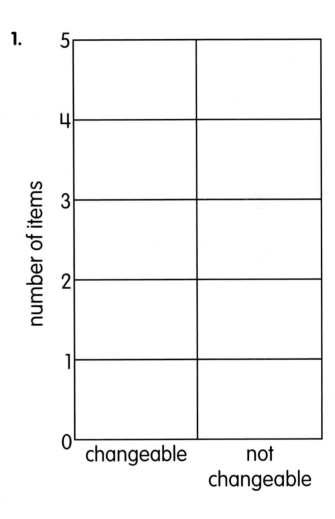

1.

number of items

5

4

3

2

1

0

changeable   not changeable

Look at the results to **distinguish** the two groups of items.

2. The easily changeable items _____.

   The items that are not changeable _____.

A trip to the museum

create: to make something new

Your class is on a field trip at a museum. Look at the signs.

Create two questions to ask at each display in the museum.

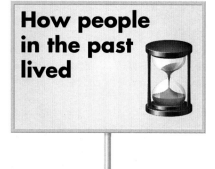

How to find any place on Earth

1. _____

   _____

2. _____

   _____

How people in the past lived

3. _____

   _____

4. _____

   _____

How people rule their land

5. _____

   _____

6. _____

   _____

A shape poem

compose: to write creatively

Choose one of these shapes:
square, circle or rectangle.

1. Draw the shape you chose.

Now **compose** an acrostic poem about your shape. Each of the letters in the shape's name starts a phrase about the shape.

2. **Compose** an acrostic poem about your shape.

Example

Three straight sides

Really pointy

Is flat

Always has angles

No curves at all

Great shape for a party hat

Looks like a tree

Easy to draw

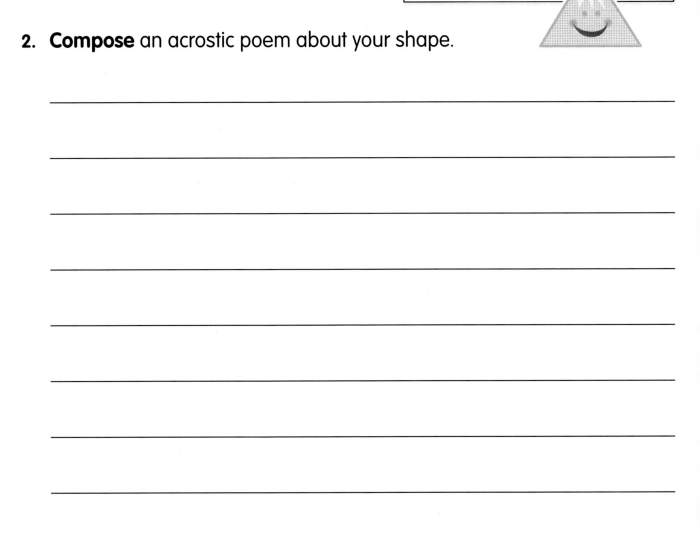

_____

_____

_____

_____

_____

_____

_____

_____

Swimming with details

represent: to show in a drawing or a graph or with a symbol

Read the text, then **represent** the information.

1. Circle the topic, or what the text is about, then underline all the details that tell about it.

The blue whale is the biggest animal in the world. It lives in water, but it is not a fish. Blue whales are mammals like you and me. They come to the surface to breathe air.

2. Now use the drawing below to **represent** the information that you circled and underlined.

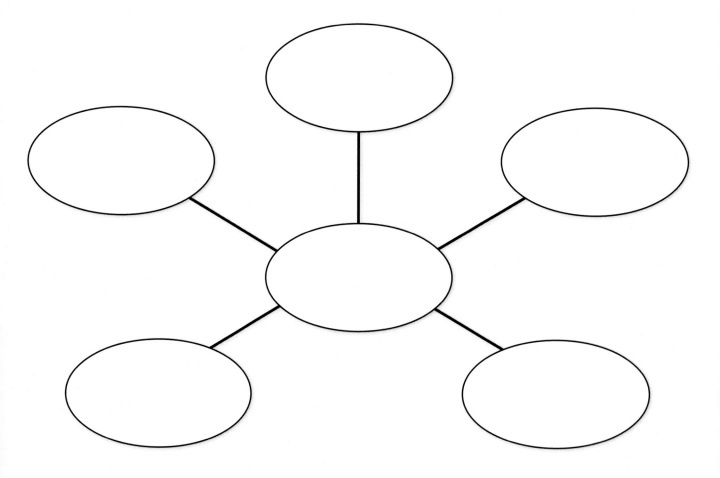

Time for ice cream!

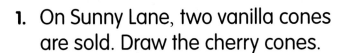

apply: to use what you know in a new way

The ice cream van is in town!

For every vanilla cone sold,
three cherry cones are sold.

Apply this information to work out
how many cones are sold at each stop.

1. On Sunny Lane, two vanilla cones
   are sold. Draw the cherry cones.

2. On Heat Street, nine cherry cones
   are sold. Draw the vanilla cones.

Animal coverings

evaluate: to judge carefully

Animals have different body coverings.
Some animals have feathers, hair, scales or a shell.
Look at the animals. Write what kind of covering each animal has.

1.

Example: A bird has   A lion has   A turtle has

feathers .   _____ .   _____ .

Evaluate the body coverings to answer the questions.

2. Which body covering would you like to have? Why?

_____

_____

3. What is one good thing about having the covering you chose?

_____

_____

4. What is one bad thing about having the covering you chose?

_____

_____

Community helpers

hypothesise: to make a good guess based on reasons

Hypothesise what might happen without community helpers. Finish the sentences.

1.  Without mechanics, _____

_____

_____.

2.  Without farmers, _____

_____

_____.

3.  Without veterinarians, _____

_____

_____.

4.  Without librarians, _____

_____

_____.

At the market

decide: to choose after thinking

Your bag holds 10 kg. **Decide** what to buy at the farmers' market.

Fresh fruit

apples	oranges	melons
3 = 1 kg	2 = 1 kg	2 kg each

Make a list of the food you bought. Show how you know your food weighs less than 10 kg.

My list	Work space

 978-1-84654-987-8 www.prim-ed.com Prim-Ed Publishing

What's going on?

infer: to use facts and what you know to learn something new

Pretend you are a detective. **Infer** what happened in these cases using the information you have.

1. Twelve cookies were in the cookie jar last night before Fran went to bed. Marcus was still in the kitchen. When Fran woke up, she noticed there were only nine cookies left.

   What can you **infer**? _____

   _____

2. Mum didn't know where Tonya and Sonya had been all day. Mum got home late, and the girls were already in bed. Mum saw a pile of new books on the floor of their room. Then she saw Sonya's library card on the bathroom shelf.

   What can you **infer**? _____

   _____

3. The air is getting cold, and most of the leaves have fallen from the trees. The squirrels are gathering nuts to store in the trees.

   What can you **infer**? _____

   _____

Meal deal

analyse: to study how parts go together

At the Dingdong Diner, you can order a tasty sandwich, bowl of soup or salad for a great price!

Analyse each row in the chart. Look at what is in the row and the total cost at the end of the row. Rows go across or up and down. Find the cost of each item. **Hint:** Start by finding the cost of the sandwich.

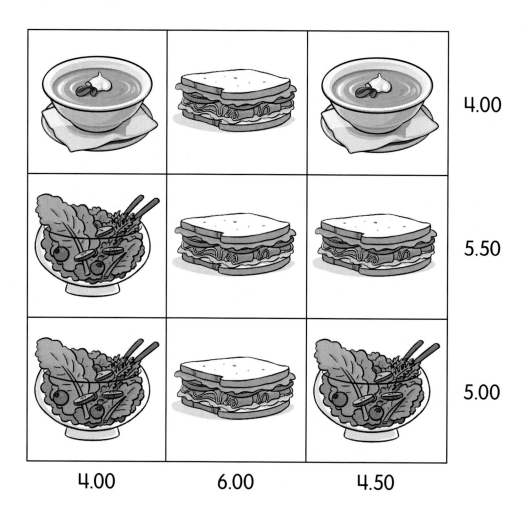

 _____  _____  _____

Cool it!

Science

rank: to put in order by value

Oscar lives in Rome. It is very hot there during summer.
In fact, it is 41°C today! Oscar wants to cool off.
Rank the things Oscar can do to cool off.
Write 1, 2, 3 or 4 in the box next to each picture.
Use the number 1 for the best thing he can do to cool off.

1.

Explain your choice for the best way to cool off.

2. _____

_____

Changing machines

distinguish: to tell the difference between things

Look at the picture from long ago and the picture from today. **Distinguish** between the two pictures.

Long ago

Today

Write two things that are the same.

1. _____

2. _____

Write two things that are different.

3. _____

_____

4. _____

_____

Up, up and away!

order: to list things in a certain way

Pretend you are a pilot from Perth, Western Australia.
Look at the map to see the cities you will fly to.

Order the cities from the closest to the farthest away.

1. _____   4. _____

2. _____   5. _____

3. _____   6. _____

Making music

support: to explain a choice

Pretend you can choose to play either the drums or the guitar.
Write about what is good and bad about each instrument.

1.  Drums are good because _____

_____

_____.

Drums are bad because _____

_____

_____.

2.  A guitar is good because _____

_____

_____.

A guitar is bad because _____

_____.

Now circle the one you choose and **support** your choice.

3. _____

_____

_____

Clever counting

organise: make something easy to understand or do

Pretend you have seven 50 tokens, seven 20 tokens and seven 10 tokens. Group the tokens so they are easy to add up. Draw a picture showing how you would **organise** the tokens.

1.

2. How much is seven 50 tokens, seven 20 tokens and seven 10 tokens? _____

3. How did your grouping make it easy to find the total?

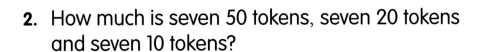

_____

_____

_____

The crozfaw

infer: to use facts and what you know to learn something new

Read about the make-believe animal. Look at the picture, then **infer** to answer the questions.

This is a crozfaw. A crozfaw is covered in feathers. The colours of its feathers can change to match any colour around it. It has two webbed feet like a duck. The crozfaw has three long antennae on its chest. It has one big eye and sharp teeth.

1. How do the crozfaw's feathers help it?

   _____

   _____

2. Do you think crozfaws can fly? Why or why not?

   _____

   _____

3. How do you think a crozfaw protects itself?

   _____

   _____

Look closely!

examine: to look at closely

Examine the close-up picture of the feature. Write what you think the feature is, then answer the question.

1. It is _____.

   How can you tell? _____

   _____

2. It is _____.

   How can you tell? _____

   _____

3. It is _____.

   How can you tell? _____

   _____

4. It is _____.

   How can you tell? _____

   _____

Rosa's new toy

design: to plan how something will look

Read, then complete the activities.

Rosa made a house for her dolls. She used craft sticks, glue and buttons. Now Rosa wants to make a new toy. **Design** a new toy with the supplies on Rosa's desk.

1. Circle the supplies you will use.

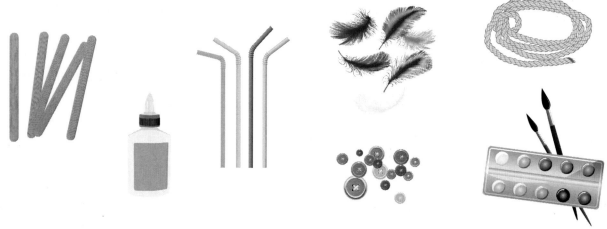

2. Design and draw the new toy.

3. Explain your design.

_____

_____

Be an editor!

justify: to give a good reason for something

Read the paragraph. Cross out the sentence that does not belong, then write to **justify** why it does not belong.

1. Aunt Mary is a great baker. She makes the best chocolate chip cookies. Aunt Mary got a new car. Every time I go to her house, she makes chocolate chip cookies for me.

_____

_____

2. Meerkats are cute. Birds are cute, too. Meerkats live in groups. Everyone in the group has a job. The sentry watches out for danger.

_____

_____

3. Have you met my really cool friend Kalil? He is always happy and never worries about anything. He's really cool. Whenever we have a test, he always says, 'Relax. Just do the best you can do'.

_____

_____

Going home

Mathematics

estimate: to give an idea about the size or value of something

Look at the bear's path to its home. Use the key to **estimate** the length of the path, then answer the question.

Key

─────
1 metre

1. Length of path

_____ metres

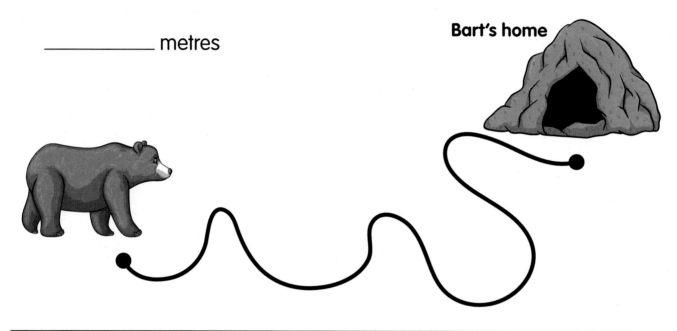

Bart's home

2. Length of path

_____ metres

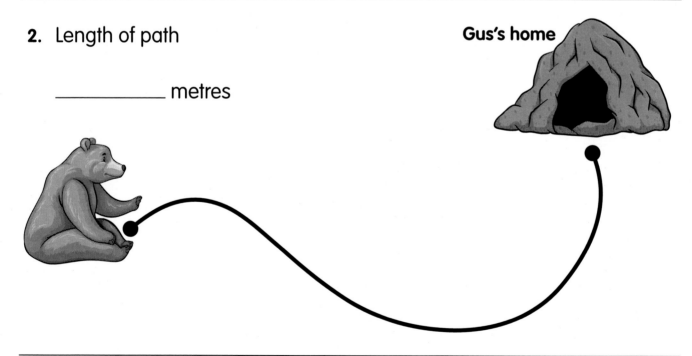

Gus's home

3. Which bear travelled the larger distance? _____

I don't believe you!

convince: to make someone agree with you

Pablo thinks that if you put water in the freezer, it will turn to ice. Heeni does not believe him.

1. How can Pablo **convince** Heeni that this is true?

_____

_____

Write two examples of other liquids that are often frozen and tell why.

2. _____

3. _____

4. Draw a picture that will also help **convince** Heeni.

Toy shopping

solve: to find an answer to a problem

Look at the pictures of the toys, then answer the questions.

Alison is shopping in New York. She finds some cool toys. Alison has $20.00, so she circles the toy she wants to buy.

Snap blocks 50 PIECES — $17.00

Racing car — Very fast! Remote control! — $60.00

1. What problem does Alison have?

_____

_____

2. How can Alison **solve** her problem?

_____

_____

_____

In the woods

determine: to work out

Some animals are hiding in the woods. Read the clues to **determine** where they are, then write their names in the correct boxes.

column	column	column

🔍 The rabbit is in the same row as the flower and the mouse.

🔍 The mouse is in the same column as the tree.

🔍 The ladybird is in the same row as the frog and the log.

🔍 The frog is in the same column as the snail.

🔍 The squirrel is in the same column as the rabbit.

Prove it!

English

prove: to show that something is true or false

Think about the statement and decide whether or not it is always true. Write a T for true or F for false next to it. If the statement is false, write an example to **prove** that the statement is false.

1. People who do not have cars always take the bus. _____

_____

_____

2. All doctors are men. _____

_____

_____

3. Things that are alive need nutrients to live. _____

_____

_____

4. Everyone has a mobile phone. _____

_____

_____

5. Each pupil should follow the school rules. _____

_____

_____

Sharing stickers

visualise: to imagine how something will look

Suppose you found a sheet of eight stickers. You want to cut the sheet in half to share it with a friend.

First **visualise** four different ways to cut the sheet into two pieces with four stickers on each piece. You can cut only along the lines.

Then use a crayon or marker on the sheets below to draw where you would cut. Colour each half of the sheet in a different colour.

1.

2.

3.

4.

The better idea

support: to explain a choice

Read the text.

The children at Hawk Primary School are trying to decide how to use an empty area of land. The Football Club wants to turn the land into a football field. The Garden Club wants to turn the land into a big vegetable garden. They made posters.

Choose one of the ideas and finish the sentence to **support** your choice.

I think the _____ Club has a better idea because

_____

_____

_____

_____ .

The longest route

infer: to use facts and what you know to learn something new

Look at the map. Emily is at her home. She needs to go to the library. She took a long route to get there.

Emily's neighbourhood

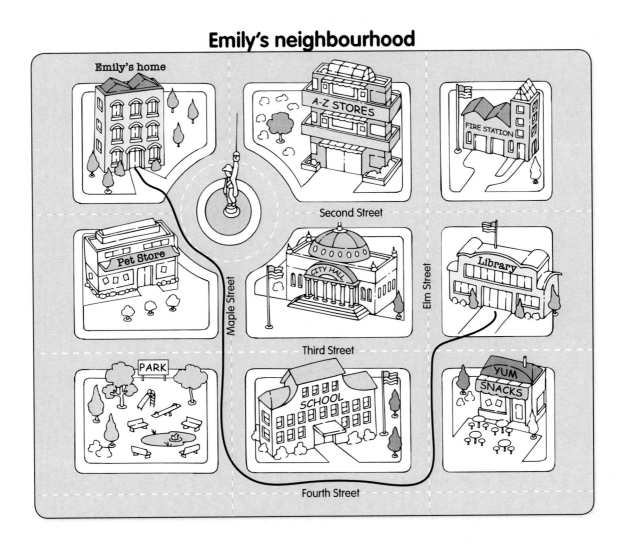

Infer why Emily took a long route. Write two reasons.

1. _____

_____

2. _____

_____

It's a party!

prepare: to get ready for something

Pretend you are planning a party. Think about what you will eat, what games and activities you will do, and what you will need.

Now **prepare** for your party. Write a list of activities, then describe how to **prepare** for each activity. The list has been started for you.

Activity	How to prepare
Announce party	Make and send invitations

Helpful ideas

suggest: to tell an idea

Read the problems, then **suggest** two ways to solve each one.

You want to go to the library and your sister wants to go shopping. Both the library and the shops close in one hour. What can you do?

1. _____

_____

2. _____

_____

You arrive at your classroom and it is locked. What can you do?

3. _____

_____

4. _____

_____

You, Terry and Shawn want to ride bikes together, but you have only two bikes among the three of you. What can you do?

5. _____

6. _____

_____

Holiday time!

determine: to work out

Sofia was leaving to go on a trip at 5.00 p.m.
At 12.00 noon, she still had a lot to do to get ready.

Read how Sofia spent her time getting ready, then **determine** how much time she had left before she had to leave.

☑ Sofia had lunch at 12.00. She finished half an hour later.

☑ Sofia washed clothes for an hour.

☑ Sofia spent an hour and a half packing.

☑ It took Sofia 45 minutes to clean the house.

☑ It took Sofia 30 minutes to water the garden.

☑ Sofia spent a quarter of an hour writing a note for the petsitter.

Work space

1. What time did Sofia finish all her work? _____

2. How much time did Sofia have before she had to leave?

_____

Broken window

solve: to find an answer to a problem

Read the text, then complete the items.

Oh no! A neighbour's ball broke Mia's window, and a storm is coming! She needs to cover the window before the rain makes her room all wet. Help Mia **solve** her problem.

1. Circle what she should use to cover the window.

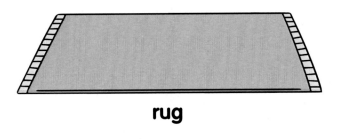

rug

wood

2. Tell why you chose that object.

_____

_____

3. Tell why you did <u>not</u> choose the other object.

_____

_____

Funfair fun

propose: to suggest an idea or a solution

Look at the picture.

Propose three rules that would help make the funfair safe, fair and fun for all.

1. _____

   _____

2. _____

   _____

3. _____

   _____

Going shopping!

persuade: to make someone want to do something

Look at Riley's money and the toys.
Complete the items.

1. How much money does Riley have? _____

2. What can Riley buy right now? _____

3. Riley wants a beach ball but wants to buy something now. What do you think he should do? **Persuade** him to do what you think.

    _____

    _____

Where's the haiku?

rewrite: to change something by writing it again

Read this poem. It is called a *haiku*. A haiku has three lines. Each line has a certain number of syllables.

Two frogs in a pond   (5 syllables)
Resting on a lily pad   (7 syllables)
Suddenly, one jumped   (5 syllables)

Now read these three poems and count the syllables. Circle the poem that is a haiku, then **rewrite** the others to make them haikus.

1. Cats are funny   _____

    Soft like a bunny   _____

    I call my cat honey   _____

2. Rain trickles outside   _____

    Droplets hit the window
    pane   _____

    Glad to be inside   _____

3. The ball bounces off
    the rim   _____

    The other team gets it   _____

    And shoots a basket for
    the win!   _____

A crawling race

prove: to show that something is true or false

A snail and a caterpillar were racing in the 100-cm crawl. For every 10 cm that the caterpillar travelled, the snail travelled 1 cm.

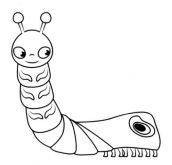

1. When the caterpillar finished the race, how many centimetres was it ahead of the snail?

   The caterpillar was _____ cm ahead of the snail.

2. Draw or write to **prove** your answer.

What's for dinner?

predict: to tell what will probably happen

Read the text, then study the food chain.

All living things need food to survive. Many animals eat plants. Many animals also eat other kinds of animals. Some scientists study what animals eat. They use a food chain to show what animals in a habitat eat. Each living thing is eaten by the animal that comes after it.

ant eats leaf   frog eats ant   snake eats frog   eagle eats snake

Predict what could happen if there were no more frogs in the habitat.

1. Without frogs, the ants _____

   _____.

2. Without frogs, the snakes _____

   _____.

Shoes of the future

design: to plan how something will look

Pretend that it is the year 2050. Your job is to make a pair of shoes that will do the things people want them to do. Read the list below to see what people want.

Shoes for the year 2050

☑ People want shoes that can fly them to work or school.

☑ People want one pair of shoes that can look different each day.

☑ People want to wear shoes that can talk.

1. **Design** a pair of shoes that will do one or more of the things people want. Draw a picture of your shoes.

2. Write to tell about the shoes you designed.

_____

_____

_____

Which car is best?

justify: to give a good reason for something

Read about the families.

> The Soto family often goes skiing in the winter. They go camping in the summer. All six of them play sports, too!

> The three Warrens help older people. They deliver food or help them do errands at least once a week.

Look at Car A and Car B and read about them.

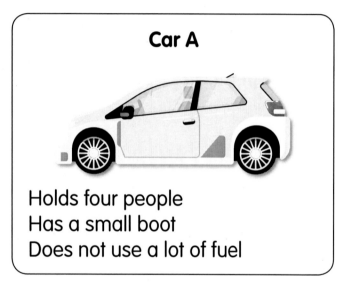

Car A

Holds four people
Has a small boot
Does not use a lot of fuel

Car B

Holds seven people
Has a big boot
Uses a lot of fuel

Both families need new cars. Which car is best for each family? Should they buy Car A or Car B? Write below to **justify** your answer.

1. I think the Soto family should buy Car _____ because _____

   _____

   _____.

2. I think the Warren family should buy Car _____ because _____

   _____

   _____.

Someone else for a day

imagine: to think of in your head

Imagine that you wake up one day as a different person. It could be someone in your family, a friend or someone else you know.

Write down who you will wake up as.

1. _____

Now think about how things would be different if you were that person. **Imagine** what a day as that person would be like and write about your day.

2. _____

_____

_____

_____

_____

_____

_____

_____

_____

_____

Out of this world

create: to make something new

Pretend you are a space explorer on a strange planet.
Everything on the planet is made out of geometric shapes!

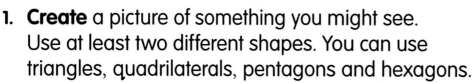

1. **Create** a picture of something you might see.
   Use at least two different shapes. You can use
   triangles, quadrilaterals, pentagons and hexagons.

2. How many of each
   shape did you use?

   △ triangle _____

   ▢ quadrilateral _____

   ⬠ pentagon _____

   ⬡ hexagon _____

3. Write about your picture. _____

   _____

   _____

That's not a fish!

work out: to find an answer

Oh no! Owen dropped a pair of scissors in his sister's fish tank. Her fish bite! Owen knows that the scissors are attracted to magnets. **Work out** how Owen can use a magnet to get the scissors out of the fish tank without putting his hand inside.

Write what Owen should do with the magnet.

_____

_____

_____

_____

What do you think?

hypothesise: to make a good guess based on reasons

Read the text.

The teeth of Queen Elizabeth I

Queen Elizabeth I had terrible teeth. Her teeth were almost black. They were decaying and in poor condition.

Hypothesise why Queen Elizabeth I had poor teeth.

_____

_____

_____

_____

What I think

English

critique: to tell what is good and bad about something

People often share what they think about things. They write about everything from restaurants to films to new toys. Read what someone wrote about a restaurant.

The Big Noodle is not so big. It is a small restaurant. The menu, however, is big. It has many different noodle dishes. I chose spaghetti and meatballs. My friend tried fried Chinese noodles.
My meal was great. The size was just right, and the meatballs were full of flavour. My friend said her noodles had too much soy sauce, though. We agreed we will go again and try two new dishes.

Critique a meal, a film or a toy.

_____

_____

_____

_____

_____

_____

_____

Prim-Ed Publishing   www.prim-ed.com   978-1-84654-987-8   **HIGHER-ORDER THINKING SKILLS – BOOK 2** | 151

Answers

Page 3

Fishy maths
determine: to work out

Read the clues to **determine** how many fish are in each tank. Draw them and write the matching addition sentence. The first one has been started for you.

1. There are 9 fish in all.
   There is 1 more fish in Tank A than in Tank B.
   $\underline{5} + \underline{4} = 9$

2. There are 10 fish in all.
   There are 2 fewer fish in Tank A than in Tank B.
   $\underline{4} + \underline{6} = 10$

3. There are 12 fish in all.
   There are 2 more fish in Tank A than in Tank B.
   $\underline{7} + \underline{5} = 12$

4. There are 11 fish in all.
   There are 3 fewer fish in Tank A than in Tank B.
   $\underline{4} + \underline{7} = 11$

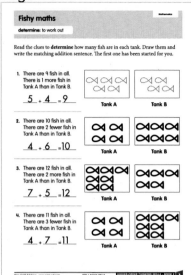

Page 5

Name it!
sort: to put things into groups

Look at the pictures.

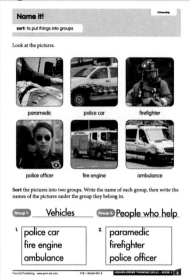

paramedic   police car   firefighter

police officer   fire engine   ambulance

Sort the pictures into two groups. Write the name of each group, then write the names of the pictures under the group they belong in.

Group 1 Vehicles
1. police car
   fire engine
   ambulance

Group 2 People who help
2. paramedic
   firefighter
   police officer

Page 6

Dress for the season
infer: to use facts and what you know to learn something new

Look at the pictures of the seasons and the clothes people wear. Draw a line to match.

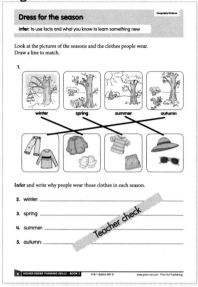

winter   spring   summer   autumn

Infer and write why people wear those clothes in each season.

2. winter: _____
3. spring: _____
4. summer: _____
5. autumn: _____

Teacher check

Page 8

Forgetful Ernie
plan: to find a good way to do something

Ernie wrote some equations, but he forgot the + and – signs! **Plan** which signs can go in the circles to make the equations true. Write the signs.

1. $5 \boxed{+} 3 \boxed{-} 2 = 6$
2. $8 \boxed{-} 4 \boxed{+} 1 = 5$
3. $7 \boxed{-} 2 \boxed{-} 2 = 3$
4. $3 \boxed{+} 9 \boxed{+} 2 = 14$

Ernie tried again. This time he remembered the signs but forgot the numbers! **Plan** which numbers can go in the circles to make the equations true. Write the numbers.

5. $\bigcirc - \bigcirc = \bigcirc$
6. $\bigcirc + \bigcirc = \bigcirc$
7. $\bigcirc + \bigcirc = \bigcirc$
8. $\bigcirc - \bigcirc = \bigcirc$

Answers will vary.

6 4
3 5

Page 9

Home sweet home
analyse: to study how parts go together

Analyse the pictures, then complete the questions.

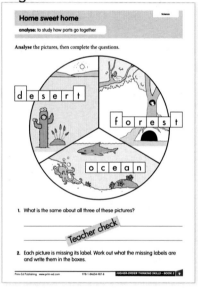

d e s e r t

f o r e s t

o c e a n

1. What is the same about all three of these pictures?
   _____ *Teacher check*

2. Each picture is missing its label. Work out what the missing labels are and write them in the boxes.

Page 10

Rules, rules, rules!
recommend: to tell the best ideas

Look at the picture.

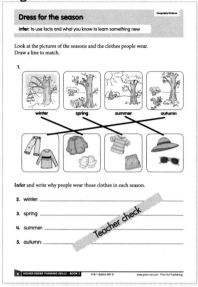

1. **Recommend** four rules for the playground. Draw a ✓ in four boxes.
   - ✓ Play well with others.
   - ☐ Run very fast.
   - ✓ Use the playground safely.
   - ✓ Stay inside the fence.
   - ☐ Yell very loudly.
   - ✓ Listen to the teacher.

2. Why are these rules the best?
   These rules keep everyone safe.

Page 11

Feathered friends
deduce: to use facts to work something out

Chirpy, Pip and Tuck each live in a different tree. Read the clues to **deduce** what kind of tree each bird lives in. As you read each clue, fill in the chart, then answer the questions.

- Chirpy does not live in the elm tree.
- Pip does not live in the oak tree.
- Tuck does not live in the pine tree.
- The bird who lives in the oak tree has the longest name.

	elm	oak	pine
Chirpy	✗	✓	✗
Pip	✗	✗	✓
Tuck	✓	✗	✗

1. Who lives in the oak tree? Chirpy
2. Who lives in the elm tree? Tuck
3. Who lives in the pine tree? Pip

Page 12

What kind of thing?
sort: to put things into groups

Look at the pictures of the items. Look at the group name on top of each box. **Sort** each of the items into a group and draw each item in the correct box.

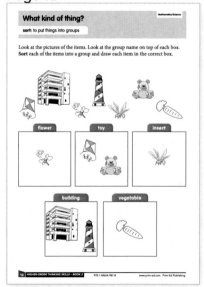

flower   toy   insect

building   vegetable

Page 13

Button patterns
analyse: to study how parts go together

Yuna is making patterns with buttons. **Analyse** the button patterns and complete the items.

1. Look at each row. How did each row change from the row above it?
   Each row has one more button than the row above it.

2. Look at the three shapes Yuna made.

   first   second   third

   How did the number of buttons in each shape change?
   She added two buttons each time.

3. Describe how the shape changed.
   It got one button higher and one button wider.

Answers

Page 14

Setting things in motion
categorise: to name a group

Look at the pictures.

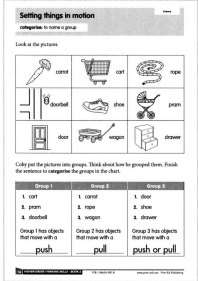

Coby put the pictures into groups. Think about how he grouped them. Finish the sentence to **categorise** the groups in the chart.

Group 1	Group 2	Group 3
1. cart	1. carrot	1. door
2. pram	2. rope	2. shoe
3. doorbell	3. wagon	3. drawer
Group 1 has objects that move with a **push**	Group 2 has objects that move with a **pull**	Group 3 has objects that move with a **push or pull**

Page 15

Road trip!
plan: to find a good way to do something

Joy wants to take a road trip through the many towns and states of Australia. **Plan** her route.
Draw an X on the map on every town Joy wants to see. Then draw a line from her home in Melbourne through the states and back home again.

Joy wants to see these towns/cities:

Newcastle   Alice Springs   Adelaide
Mount Isa   Kalgoorlie   Cairns

1.

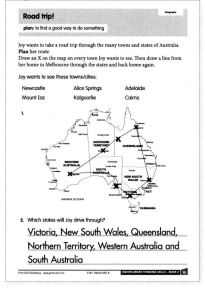

2. Which states will Joy drive through?

Victoria, New South Wales, Queensland, Northern Territory, Western Australia and South Australia

Page 16

New plants
arrange: to put in the best place

Help Dilip **arrange** his new plants in his garden. Read about each plant, then look at Dilip's garden. Write the name of each plant in the spot where it will grow best in his garden.

wood fern Needs shade and lots of water. Mist on hot days.

ivy Grows to 10 m in sunshine. Will climb up or sideways.

lemon tree Likes sunshine and damp soil.

ivy   lemon tree   wood fern

Page 17

Putting it all together
assemble: to put parts together

Put the letters together to **assemble** words. Write each word.

1. l e d b   bed
2. s i m w   swim
3. o k b o   book
4. y p l a   play

Put the words together to **assemble** sentences.

5. grass farm the eat horses the on
The horses eat grass on the farm./
The horses on the farm eat grass.

6. smiled he baby when me the saw
The baby smiled when he saw me./
When the baby saw me, he smiled.

7. my wonder boots I are where
I wonder where my boots are.

8. the camels you show watch about should
You should watch the show about camels.

Page 18

Coin patterns
predict: to tell what will probably happen

Jen and Ian got some coins from their piggy banks, then they each made a pattern with **10 coins**. Look at how their patterns start. **Predict** which pattern will have the greater value with all 10 coins, then write or draw to check your prediction.

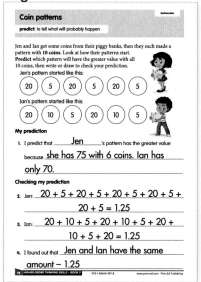

Jen's pattern started like this:

20   5   20   5   20   5

Ian's pattern started like this:

20   10   5   20   10   5

My prediction

1. I predict that ___Jen___'s pattern has the greater value because she has 75 with 6 coins. Ian has only 70.

Checking my prediction

2. Jen: 20 + 5 + 20 + 5 + 20 + 5 + 20 + 5 + 20 + 5 = 1.25
3. Ian: 20 + 10 + 5 + 20 + 10 + 5 + 20 + 10 + 5 + 20 = 1.25
4. I found out that Jen and Ian have the same amount – 1.25

Page 19

Naming places
hypothesise: to make a good guess based on reasons

Look at the pictures. How do you think the places got their names? **Hypothesise** why and how the towns got their name.

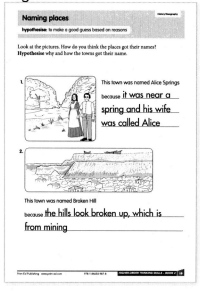

1. This town was named Alice Springs because it was near a spring and his wife was called Alice

2. This town was named Broken Hill because the hills look broken up, which is from mining

Page 20

In the city
support: to explain a choice

Look at the picture. Find the things that do not belong. Circle them.

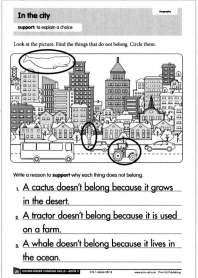

Write a reason to **support** why each thing does not belong.

1. A cactus doesn't belong because it grows in the desert.
2. A tractor doesn't belong because it is used on a farm.
3. A whale doesn't belong because it lives in the ocean.

Page 21

Don't be late!
order: to list things in a certain way

Look at the map of a neighbourhood. If all the children leave for school at the same time, who will arrive first? Who will arrive last?

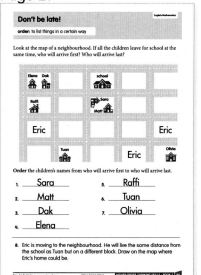

Order the children's names from who will arrive first to who will arrive last.

1. Sara
2. Matt
3. Dak
4. Elena
5. Raffi
6. Tuan
7. Olivia

8. Eric is moving to the neighbourhood. He will live the same distance from the school as Tuan but on a different block. Draw on the map where Eric's home could be.

Page 22

Hiding synonyms
rewrite: to change something by writing it again

Synonyms are words that mean the same thing. Think of a synonym that can be used to **rewrite** the underlined word in each sentence and write it on the line. Then find and circle the synonym in the word search puzzle. If you can't find the synonym you wrote, try a different synonym.

1. Alma is sick today.   ill
2. Start on page 12.   begin
3. He's scared of the dark.   afraid
4. We are happy that you came.   glad
5. They moved into a new house.   home

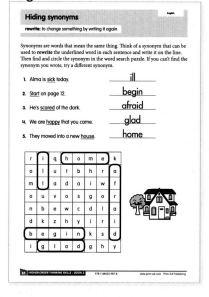

r	i	q	h	o	m	e	k
o	l	u	t	b	h	r	a
m	l	a	d	a	i	w	f
o	u	v	o	s	g	o	r
n	b	e	w	c	d	l	a
d	k	z	h	y	i	r	i
b	e	g	i	n	k	s	d
i	g	l	a	d	g	h	y

Answers

Page 24

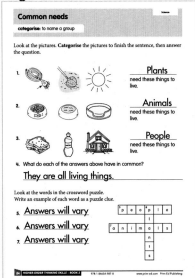

Common needs

categorise: to name a group

Look at the pictures. **Categorise** the pictures to finish the sentence, then answer the question.

1. **Plants** need these things to live.
2. **Animals** need these things to live.
3. **People** need these things to live.

4. What do each of the answers above have in common?

They are all living things.

Look at the words in the crossword puzzle.
Write an example of each word as a puzzle clue.

5. **Answers will vary**
6. **Answers will vary**
7. **Answers will vary**

Crossword: p e o p l e / a n i m a l s / plants

Page 27

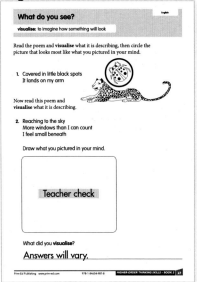

What do you see?

visualise: to imagine how something will look

Read the poem and **visualise** what it is describing, then circle the picture that looks most like what you pictured in your mind.

1. Covered in little black spots
   It lands on my arm

Now read this poem and **visualise** what it is describing.

2. Reaching to the sky
   More windows than I can count
   I feel small beneath

Draw what you pictured in your mind.

Teacher check

What did you **visualise**?

Answers will vary.

Page 29

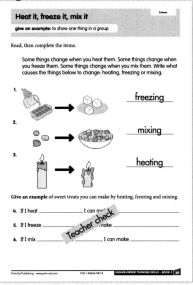

Heat it, freeze it, mix it

give an example: to show one thing in a group

Read, then complete the items.

Some things change when you heat them. Some things change when you freeze them. Some things change when you mix them. Write what causes the things below to change: heating, freezing or mixing.

1. **freezing**
2. **mixing**
3. **heating**

Give an example of sweet treats you can make by heating, freezing and mixing.

4. If I heat _____ I can make _____
5. If I freeze _____ I can make _____
6. If I mix _____, I can make

Teacher check

Page 30

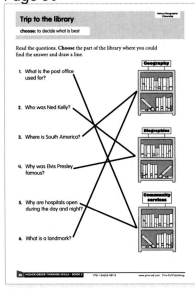

Trip to the library

choose: to decide what is best

Read the questions. **Choose** the part of the library where you could find the answer and draw a line.

1. What is the post office used for?
2. Who was Ned Kelly?
3. Where is South America?
4. Why was Elvis Presley famous?
5. Why are hospitals open during the day and night?
6. What is a landmark?

Geography / Biographies / Community services

Page 31

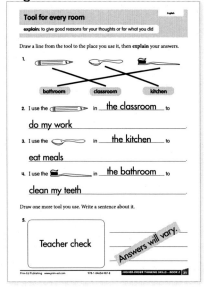

Tool for every room

explain: to give good reasons for your thoughts or for what you did

Draw a line from the tool to the place you use it, then **explain** your answers.

1. bathroom / classroom / kitchen

2. I use the ✏ in **the classroom** to **do my work**

3. I use the 🥄 in **the kitchen** to **eat meals**

4. I use the 🪥 in **the bathroom** to **clean my teeth**

Draw one more tool you use. Write a sentence about it.

5. **Teacher check**   Answers will vary.

Page 32

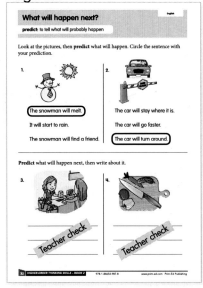

What will happen next?

predict: to tell what will probably happen

Look at the pictures, then **predict** what will happen. Circle the sentence with your prediction.

1. **The snowman will melt.**
   It will start to rain.
   The snowman will find a friend.

2. The car will stay where it is.
   The car will go faster.
   The car will turn around.

Predict what will happen next, then write about it.

3. **Teacher check**
4. **Teacher check**

Page 33

The bugs' ball

plan: to find a good way to do something

Read and solve the problem.

Pretend some insects and spiders went to a fancy dance. Insects have six legs, and spiders have eight. If there were 40 dancing legs, how many insects and spiders were there?

1. **Plan** how you will solve the problem. Write or draw your ideas in the box.

Teacher check

2. There were **4** insects and **2** spiders at the dance.

Page 35

Wrong direction

rewrite: to change something by writing it again

Peter told Risa where the park was, but she is lost. **Rewrite** Peter's directions.

Peter's directions	Your directions
The park is	The park is
N of the library	N of **Oak Street**
S of the post office	S of **the library**
E of Oak Street	E of **the fire station**
W of the school	W of **the police station**

Page 37

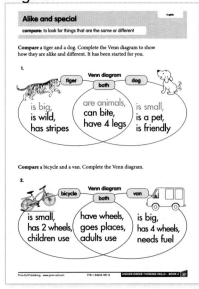

Alike and special

compare: to look for things that are the same or different

Compare a tiger and a dog. Complete the Venn diagram to show how they are alike and different. It has been started for you.

1. Venn diagram — tiger / both / dog
   is big, is wild, has stripes | are animals, can bite, have 4 legs | is small, is a pet, is friendly

Compare a bicycle and a van. Complete the Venn diagram.

2. Venn diagram — bicycle / both / van
   is small, has 2 wheels, children use | have wheels, goes places, adults use | is big, has 4 wheels, needs fuel

Answers

Page 38

Farmer Joe's animals

order: to list things in a certain way

Farmer Joe's animals stand in a row. Read the clues to help you **order** where they are, then write the names of the animals on the correct lines.

○ Billy is between Flo and Ace.

○ Muffin is between Lucky and Ace.

○ Ace and Flo eat hay.

○ Lucky sleeps by Farmer Joe's bed at night.

1. Lucky   2. Muffin   3. Ace   4. Billy   5. Flo

Page 39

Knock, knock, who's there?

Justify: to give a good reason for something

Look at the pictures. Who do you think lives in each of these animal homes? **Justify** your answers.

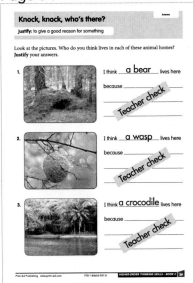

1. I think _a bear_ lives here because _Teacher check_

2. I think _a wasp_ lives here because _Teacher check_

3. I think _a crocodile_ lives here because _Teacher check_

Page 40

Then and now

distinguish: to tell the difference between things

Look at the pictures. **Distinguish** between how the city looked in the past and how it looks today.

1. Label each picture with **past** or **today**.

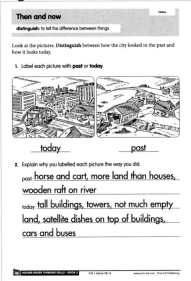

today   past

2. Explain why you labelled each picture the way you did.

past: horse and cart, more land than houses, wooden raft on river

today: tall buildings, towers, not much empty land, satellite dishes on top of buildings, cars and buses

Page 41

Reusing things

suggest: to tell an idea

The pictures below show things we use every day. Write how each object is usually used, then **suggest** two other ways the object can be used.

1. is used to: hold eggs — other uses: _Teacher check_

2. is used to: hold cereal — other uses: _Teacher check_

3. is used to: read articles or stories — other uses: _Teacher check_

4. is used to: hold papers together — other uses: _Teacher check_

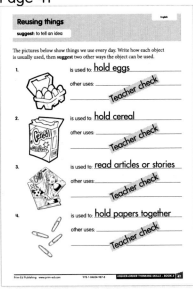

Page 42

Getting to know you

interview: to ask someone questions about his or her life

Look at the people. Draw a line matching each person with his or her job.

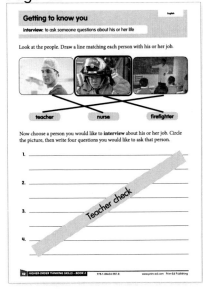

teacher   nurse   firefighter

Now choose a person you would like to **interview** about his or her job. Circle the picture, then write four questions you would like to ask that person.

1.
2.
3.
4.

Teacher check

Page 43

Chunky chocolates

deduce: to use facts to work something out

Read the text and look at the pictures of the boxes.

At the Chunky Chocolate Factory, chocolates are sold in round boxes and square boxes. All the round boxes have the same number of chocolates. All the square boxes have the same number of chocolates.

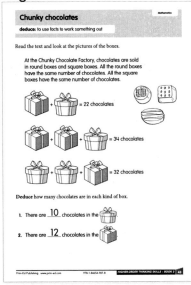

+ = 22 chocolates

+ + = 34 chocolates

+ = 32 chocolates

Deduce how many chocolates are in each kind of box.

1. There are _10_ chocolates in the ⬭.

2. There are _12_ chocolates in the ⬜.

Page 45

Musical zoo pens

visualise: to imagine how something will look

All the animals are moving to different pens. **Visualise** where they will end up.

The zebras and the lions will trade places.
The bear will move one pen to the left.
The giraffes will move in with the elephants.
The elephants will move into the empty pen.

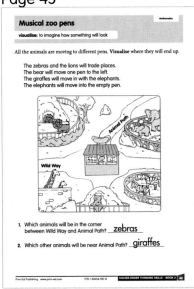

1. Which animals will be in the corner between Wild Way and Animal Path? _zebras_

2. Which other animals will be near Animal Path? _giraffes_

Page 47

What is it?

describe: to tell how something looks, sounds, smells or feels

You and a friend are playing a guessing game. Your friend **describes** something without saying its name. You guess what it is.

1. It's very big. It has a long trunk and big, floppy ears.

What is it? _an elephant_

Now it's your turn to **describe** things to your friend. Write three things about each object. Don't use the name of the object.

2.
3.
4.
Answers will vary.

5.
6.
7.
Answers will vary.

Page 48

On target

plan: to find a good way to do something

Lucia shot three arrows. She scored 62 points. Each arrow hit a different number on the target. What numbers did the arrows land on? **Plan** how you will solve the problem, then use your plan to find the answer.

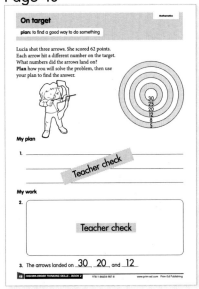

My plan

1.
Teacher check

My work

2.
Teacher check

3. The arrows landed on _30_ , _20_ and _12_ .

Answers

Page 51

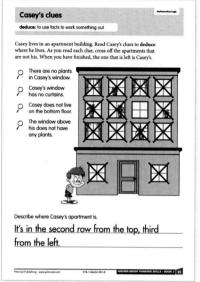

Casey's clues

Mathematics/Logic

deduce: to use facts to work something out

Casey lives in an apartment building. Read Casey's clues to **deduce** where he lives. As you read each clue, cross off the apartments that are not his. When you have finished, the one that is left is Casey's.

- There are no plants in Casey's window.
- Casey's window has no curtains.
- Casey does not live on the bottom floor.
- The window above his does not have any plants.

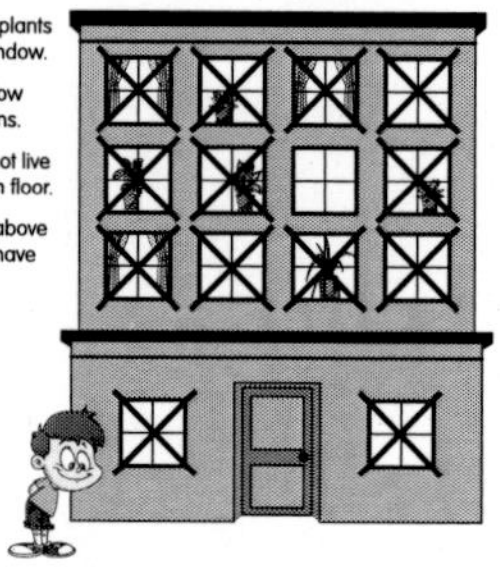

Describe where Casey's apartment is.

It's in the second row from the top, third from the left.

Prim-Ed Publishing www.prim-ed.com 978-1-84654-987-8 HIGHER-ORDER THINKING SKILLS – BOOK 2 51

Page 53

Juggling fun

Mathematics

form: to bring parts together to make something

Use the numbers on the balls to **form** three-digit numbers that match the clues.

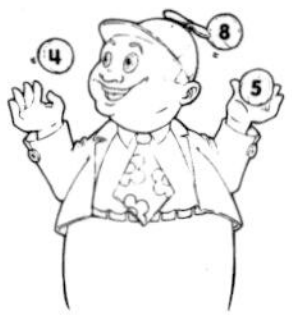

1. the largest number 854
2. the smallest number 458
3. the largest number with 8 in the tens place 584
4. the largest odd number that is less than 600 485

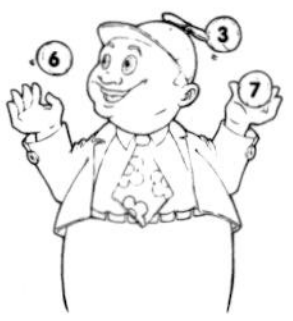

5. the largest odd number 763
6. the smallest number with 3 in the ones place 673
7. the smallest number that is greater than 500 637
8. the smallest even number 376

Prim-Ed Publishing www.prim-ed.com 978-1-84654-987-8 HIGHER-ORDER THINKING SKILLS – BOOK 2 53

Page 55

All about Brandon

History

arrange: to put in the best place

These pictures show Brandon at different ages. Draw a line from each picture to the timeline to **arrange** the pictures from youngest to oldest. Write Brandon's age in the circles. Then answer the question.

1.

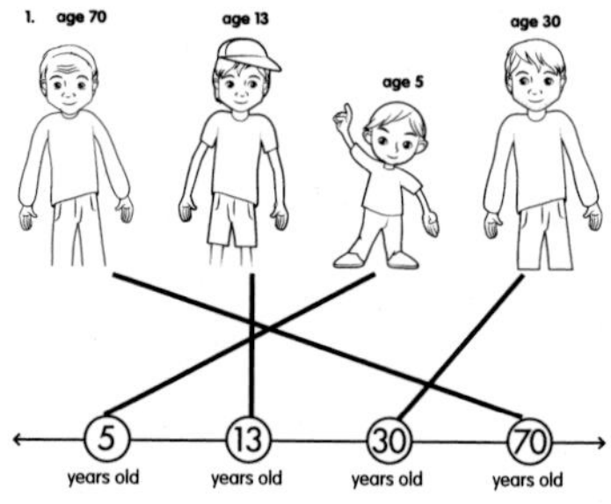

age 70
age 13
age 5
age 30
5 years old
13 years old
30 years old
70 years old

2. How did you know how to **arrange** the pictures?

Teacher check

Prim-Ed Publishing www.prim-ed.com 978-1-84654-987-8 HIGHER-ORDER THINKING SKILLS – BOOK 2 55

Page 56

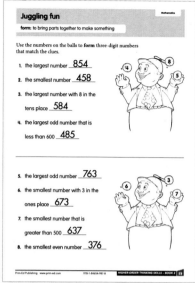

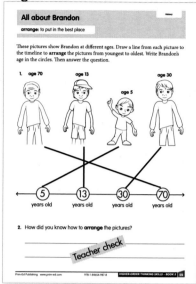

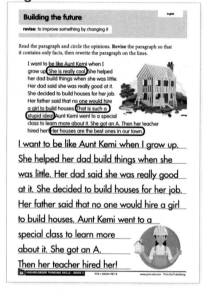

Building the future

English

revise: to improve something by changing it

Read the paragraph and circle the opinions. **Revise** the paragraph so that it contains only facts, then rewrite the paragraph on the lines.

I want to be like Aunt Kemi when I grow up. She is really cool. She helped her dad build things when she was little. Her dad said she was really good at it. She decided to build houses for her job. Her father said that no one would hire a girl to build houses. That is such a stupid idea! Aunt Kemi went to a special class to learn more about it. She got an A. Then her teacher hired her! Her houses are the best ones in our town.

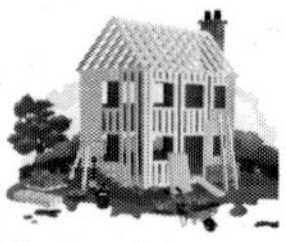

I want to be like Aunt Kemi when I grow up. She helped her dad build things when she was little. Her dad said she was really good at it. She decided to build houses for her job. Her father said that no one would hire a girl to build houses. Aunt Kemi went to a special class to learn more about it. She got an A. Then her teacher hired her!

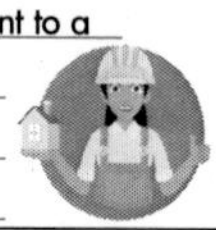

56 HIGHER-ORDER THINKING SKILLS – BOOK 2 978-1-84654-987-8 www.prim-ed.com Prim-Ed Publishing

Page 58

Stack the apples

Mathematics

arrange: to put in the best place

Pretend you work at a supermarket. You need to put ten apples in a triangle shape. The apples are red, yellow and green. No apple can touch another apple of the same colour. Show how you can **arrange** the apples below. Colour them red, yellow or green.

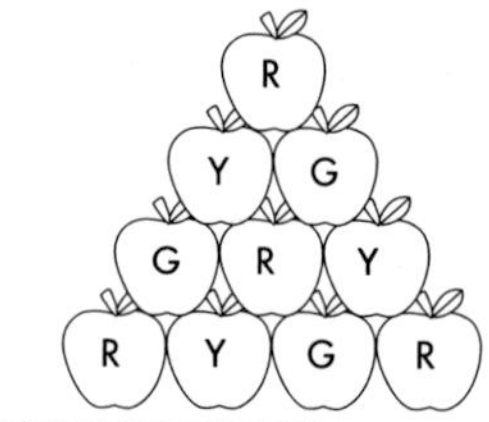

R
Y G
G R Y
R Y G R

1. Write how many you have of each apple.

red 4 yellow 3 green 3

2. Is there more than one way to **arrange** the apples? yes

Explain your answer. You can start with a different colour on top. That will change the way the other colours are stacked.

58 HIGHER-ORDER THINKING SKILLS – BOOK 2 978-1-84654-987-8 www.prim-ed.com Prim-Ed Publishing

Page 59

Lift off!

Science

deduce: to use facts to work something out

Read the clues about something in space. **Deduce** what it is and finish the sentence.

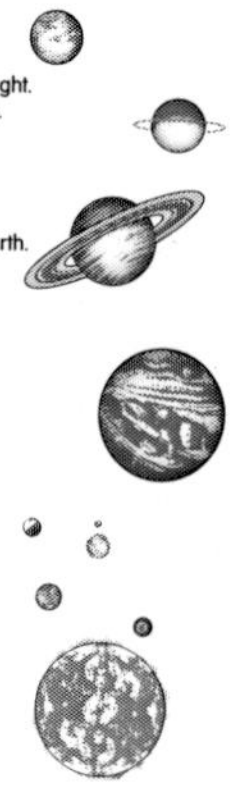

1. I am a ball of hot gas. I look like a tiny dot of light. People like to make a wish when they see me.

   I am a s t a r (4, 3)

2. I do not make my own light. I travel around Earth. I am big and round.

   I am a m o o n (1)

3. We travel around the sun. There are eight of us. We all spin around.

   We are p l a n e t s (5, 7)

4. I have seven continents. I have five oceans. I am home to people and animals.

   I am planet E a r t h (6, 2)

Write the numbered letters to finish the sentence.

5. The rocket flies to o u t e r s p a c e (1 2 3 4 5 6 7)

Prim-Ed Publishing www.prim-ed.com 978-1-84654-987-8 HIGHER-ORDER THINKING SKILLS – BOOK 2 59

Page 61

A busy morning

English/Mathematics

order: to list things in a certain way

Read the list of small jobs Mrs Brown has to do, then look at the map. In which order should she do her jobs? Put a number next to each job on the list to **order** them.

Jobs

1. Buy chicken and carrots. 7
2. Take her son to school. 2
3. Buy stamps. 4
4. Return library books. 3
5. Take Mr Lee some soup. 1
6. Buy food for the fish. 5
7. Buy a hammer. 6

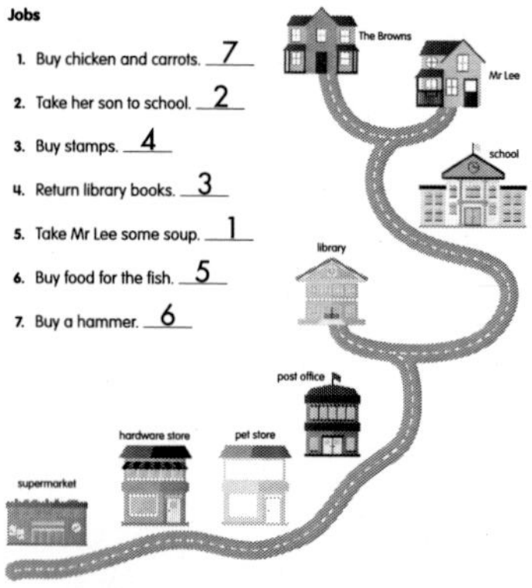

The Browns
Mr Lee
school
library
post office
hardware store
pet store
supermarket

Prim-Ed Publishing www.prim-ed.com 978-1-84654-987-8 HIGHER-ORDER THINKING SKILLS – BOOK 2 61

Page 62

List mix-up

English

sort: to put things into groups

Mr Edo's weekly spelling lists have words on the same topic. Amy's spelling cards from three lists have got mixed up. Look at the spelling cards to work out the topics of the spelling lists. Write the topics on the lists, then draw lines to **sort** the cards.

Spelling lists

1. topic: Animals
   1.
   2.
   3.
   4.
2. topic: Tools
   1.
   2.
   3.
   4.
3. topic: Food
   1.
   2.
   3.
   4.

Spelling cards

- monkey
- spanner
- pasta
- hammer
- owl
- pizza
- lion
- snake
- screwdriver
- hamburger
- cake
- saw

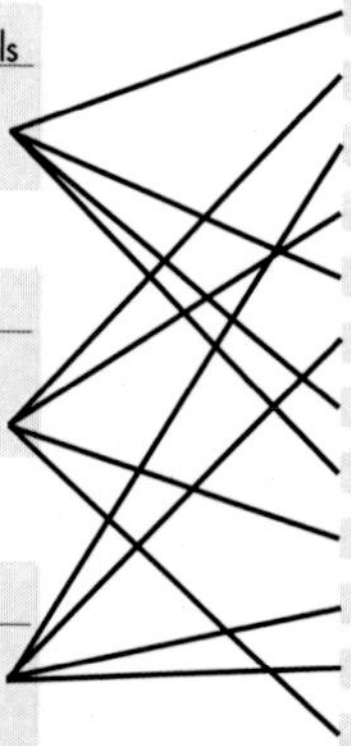

62 HIGHER-ORDER THINKING SKILLS – BOOK 2 978-1-84654-987-8 www.prim-ed.com Prim-Ed Publishing

Page 63

Mystery numbers

Mathematics

deduce: to use facts to work something out

A magician wrote three numbers on a piece of paper, then he put the paper in his hat. **Deduce** which numbers he wrote. Read the clues to help you work out the mystery numbers.

- The numbers are between 300 and 350.
- The numbers are odd and are three digits long.
- The sum of the three digits in each number is even.
- The tens digit is greater than the ones digit.

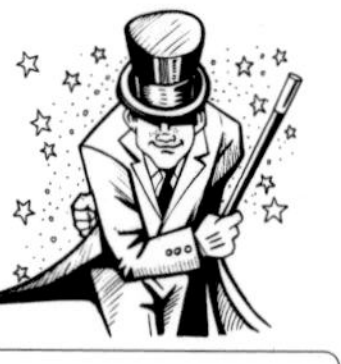

Work space

What are the numbers? 321 341 343

Prim-Ed Publishing www.prim-ed.com 978-1-84654-987-8 HIGHER-ORDER THINKING SKILLS – BOOK 2 63

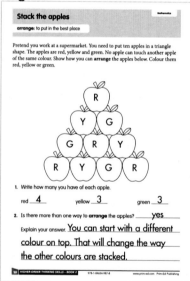

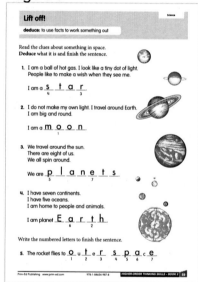

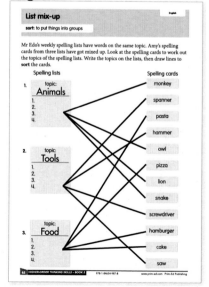

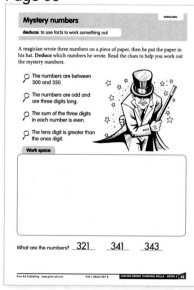

Answers

Page 67

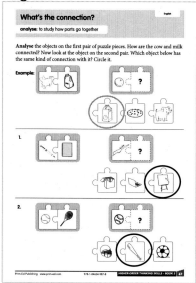

What's the connection?

analyse: to study how parts go together

Analyse the objects on the first pair of puzzle pieces. How are the cow and milk connected? Now look at the object on the second pair. Which object below has the same kind of connection with it? Circle it.

Page 68

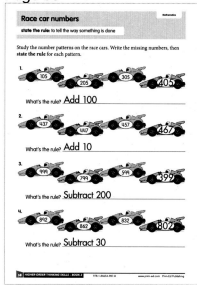

Race car numbers

state the rule: to tell the way something is done

Study the number patterns on the race cars. Write the missing numbers, then **state the rule** for each pattern.

1. 105, 205, 305, 405
What's the rule? Add 100

2. 437, 447, 457, 467
What's the rule? Add 10

3. 999, 899, 799, 699, 599, 399
What's the rule? Subtract 200

4. 892, 862, 832, 802
What's the rule? Subtract 30

Page 70

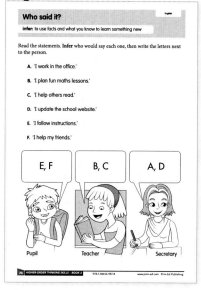

Who said it?

infer: to use facts and what you know to learn something new

Read the statements. **Infer** who would say each one, then write the letters next to the person.

A. 'I work in the office.'
B. 'I plan fun maths lessons.'
C. 'I help others read.'
D. 'I update the school website.'
E. 'I follow instructions.'
F. 'I help my friends.'

E, F — Pupil   B, C — Teacher   A, D — Secretary

Page 72

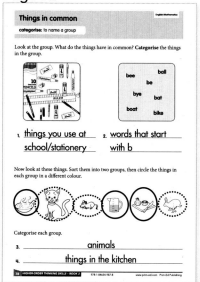

Things in common

categorise: to name a group

Look at the group. What do the things have in common? **Categorise** the things in the group.

bee, ball, be, bye, bat, boat, bike

1. things you use at school/stationery
2. words that start with b

Now look at these things. Sort them into two groups, then circle the things in each group in a different colour.

Categorise each group.

3. animals
4. things in the kitchen

Page 77

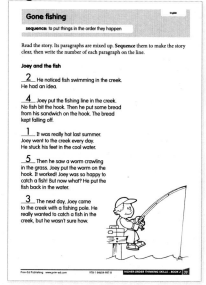

Gone fishing

sequence: to put things in the order they happen

Read the story. Its paragraphs are mixed up. **Sequence** them to make the story clear, then write the number of each paragraph on the line.

Joey and the fish

2 He noticed fish swimming in the creek. He had an idea.

4 Joey put the fishing line in the creek. No fish bit the hook. Then he put some bread from his sandwich on the hook. The bread kept falling off.

1 It was really hot last summer. Joey went to the creek every day. He stuck his feet in the cool water.

5 Then he saw a worm crawling in the grass. Joey put the worm on the hook. It worked! Joey was so happy to catch a fish! But now what? He put the fish back in the water.

3 The next day, Joey came to the creek with a fishing pole. He really wanted to catch a fish in the creek, but he wasn't sure how.

Page 78

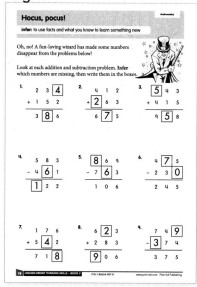

Hocus, pocus!

infer: to use facts and what you know to learn something new

Oh, no! A fun-loving wizard has made some numbers disappear from the problems below!

Look at each addition and subtraction problem. **Infer** which numbers are missing, then write them in the boxes.

1.
$$2\ 3\ [4]$$
$$+\ 1\ 5\ 2$$
$$3\ 8\ 6$$

2.
$$4\ 1\ 2$$
$$+\ [2]\ 6\ 3$$
$$6\ 7\ 5$$

3.
$$[5]\ 4\ 3$$
$$+\ 4\ 1\ 5$$
$$9\ [5]\ 8$$

4.
$$5\ 8\ 3$$
$$-\ 4\ [6]\ 1$$
$$[1]\ 2\ 2$$

5.
$$8\ 6\ 9$$
$$-\ 7\ 6\ 3$$
$$1\ 0\ 6$$

6.
$$4\ [7]\ 5$$
$$-\ 2\ 3\ 0$$
$$2\ 4\ 5$$

7.
$$1\ 7\ 6$$
$$+\ 5\ [4]\ 2$$
$$7\ 1\ 8$$

8.
$$6\ [2]\ 3$$
$$+\ 2\ 8\ 3$$
$$9\ 0\ 6$$

9.
$$7\ 4\ [9]$$
$$-\ 3\ 7\ 4$$
$$3\ 7\ 5$$

Page 79

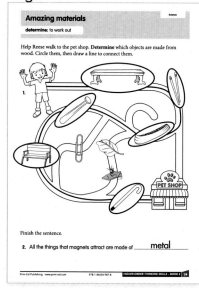

Amazing materials

determine: to work out

Help Reese walk to the pet shop. **Determine** which objects are made from wood. Circle them, then draw a line to connect them.

Finish the sentence.

2. All the things that magnets attract are made of __metal__

Page 82

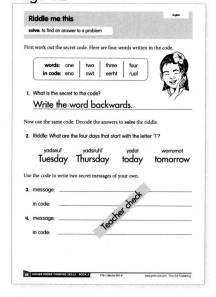

Riddle me this

solve: to find an answer to a problem

First work out the secret code. Here are four words written in the code.

words:	one	two	three	four
in code:	eno	owt	eerht	ruof

1. What is the secret to the code?
Write the word backwards.

Now use the same code. Decode the answers to **solve** the riddle.

2. Riddle: What are the four days that start with the letter 'T'?

yadseuT — Tuesday   yadsruhT — Thursday   yadot — today   worromot — tomorrow

Use the code to write two secret messages of your own.

3. message: _____
in code: _____

4. message: _____
in code: _____

Teacher check

Page 83

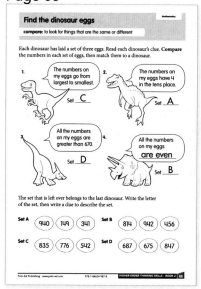

Find the dinosaur eggs

compare: to look for things that are the same or different

Each dinosaur has laid a set of three eggs. Read each dinosaur's clue. **Compare** the numbers in each set of eggs, then match them to a dinosaur.

1. The numbers on my eggs go from largest to smallest. Set C
2. The numbers on my eggs have 4 in the tens place. Set A
3. All the numbers on my eggs are greater than 670. Set D
4. All the numbers on my eggs are even. Set B

The set that is left over belongs to the last dinosaur. Write the letter of the set, then write a clue to describe the set.

Set A: 940, 149, 341
Set B: 814, 942, 456
Set C: 835, 776, 542
Set D: 687, 675, 847

Answers

Page 88

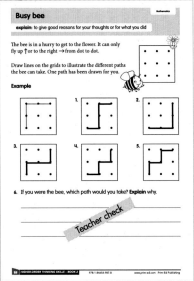

Busy bee

explain: to give good reasons for your thoughts or for what you did

The bee is in a hurry to get to the flower. It can only fly up ↑ or to the right → from dot to dot.

Draw lines on the grids to illustrate the different paths the bee can take. One path has been drawn for you.

Example

6. If you were the bee, which path would you take? **Explain** why.

Teacher check

Page 89

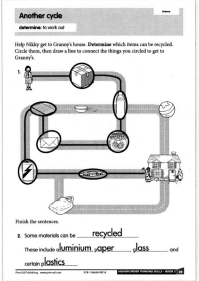

Another cycle

determine: to work out

Help Nikky get to Granny's house. **Determine** which items can be recycled. Circle them, then draw a line to connect the things you circled to get to Granny's.

Finish the sentences.

2. Some materials can be _____ recycled

These include aluminium, paper, glass, and certain plastics.

Page 91

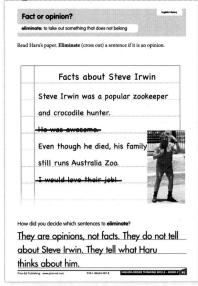

Fact or opinion?

eliminate: to take out something that does not belong

Read Haru's paper. **Eliminate** (cross out) a sentence if it is an opinion.

> ### Facts about Steve Irwin
> Steve Irwin was a popular zookeeper and crocodile hunter.
> ~~He was awesome.~~
> Even though he died, his family still runs Australia Zoo.
> ~~I would love their job!~~

How did you decide which sentences to **eliminate**?

They are opinions, not facts. They do not tell about Steve Irwin. They tell what Haru thinks about him.

Page 94

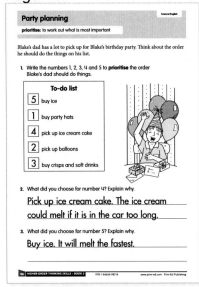

Party planning

prioritise: to work out what is most important

Blake's dad has a lot to pick up for Blake's birthday party. Think about the order he should do the things on his list.

1. Write the numbers 1, 2, 3, 4 and 5 to **prioritise** the order Blake's dad should do things.

To-do list

5	buy ice
1	buy party hats
4	pick up ice cream cake
2	pick up balloons
3	buy crisps and soft drinks

2. What did you choose for number 4? Explain why.

Pick up ice cream cake. The ice cream could melt if it is in the car too long.

3. What did you choose for number 5? Explain why.

Buy ice. It will melt the fastest.

Page 97

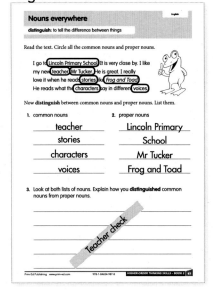

Nouns everywhere

distinguish: to tell the difference between things

Read the text. Circle all the common nouns and proper nouns.

I go to (Lincoln Primary School). It is very close by. I like my new (teacher) (Mr Tucker). He is great. I really love it when he reads (stories) like (Frog and Toad). He reads what the (characters) say in different (voices).

Now **distinguish** between common nouns and proper nouns. List them.

1. common nouns
- teacher
- stories
- characters
- voices

2. proper nouns
- Lincoln Primary School
- Mr Tucker
- Frog and Toad

3. Look at both lists of nouns. Explain how you **distinguished** common nouns from proper nouns.

Teacher check

Page 98

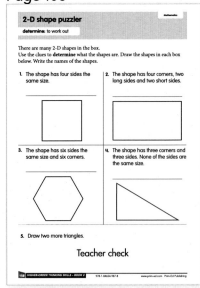

Row, raw, row

organise: make something easy to understand or do

A family is going rowing. They must follow these rules.

☑ The four family members will use two boats.

☑ Each boat will carry the same weight.

Organise who will ride together. Add the weights to make sure each total is the same, then write the names next to the boat.

Dad 69 kg   Mum 61 kg   Katie 28 kg   Scamp 20 kg

Work space

1. Dad and Scamp

2. Mum and Katie

Page 102

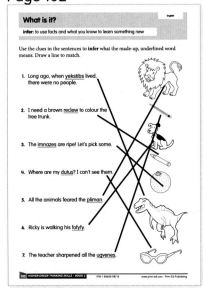

What is it?

infer: to use facts and what you know to learn something new

Use the clues in the sentences to **infer** what the made-up, underlined word means. Draw a line to match.

1. Long ago, when yekstibs lived, there were no people.

2. I need a brown reclew to colour the tree trunk.

3. The imnazes are ripe! Let's pick some.

4. Where are my dutus? I can't see them.

5. All the animals feared the pliman.

6. Ricky is walking his fofyfy.

7. The teacher sharpened all the ugvenes.

Page 103

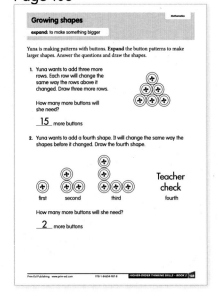

Growing shapes

expand: to make something bigger

Yuna is making patterns with buttons. **Expand** the button patterns to make larger shapes. Answer the questions and draw the shapes.

1. Yuna wants to add three more rows. Each row will change the same way the rows above it changed. Draw three more rows.

How many more buttons will she need?

__15__ more buttons

2. Yuna wants to add a fourth shape. It will change the same way the shapes before it changed. Draw the fourth shape.

first   second   third   fourth

Teacher check

How many more buttons will she need?

__2__ more buttons

Page 108

2-D shape puzzler

determine: to work out

There are many 2-D shapes in the box. Use the clues to **determine** what the shapes are. Draw the shapes in each box below. Write the names of the shapes.

1. The shape has four sides the same size.

2. The shape has four corners, two long sides and two short sides.

3. The shape has six sides the same size and six corners.

4. The shape has three corners and three sides. None of the sides are the same size.

5. Draw two more triangles.

Teacher check

Answers

Page 109

What gives?

distinguish: to tell the difference between things

Ms Salib's class tested items in their classroom to see if they can be changed. Look at the results. Fill in the graph to show the results, then finish the sentences to **distinguish** the two groups of items.

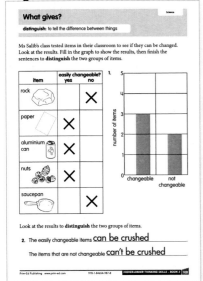

item	easily changeable?	
	yes	no
rock		✗
paper	✗	
aluminium can	✗	
nuts	✗	
saucepan		✗

Look at the results to **distinguish** the two groups of items.

2. The easily changeable items **can be crushed**

The items that are not changeable **can't be crushed**

Page 112

Swimming with details

represent: to show in a drawing or a graph or with a symbol

Read the text, then **represent** the information.

1. Circle the topic, or what the text is about, then underline all the details that tell about it.

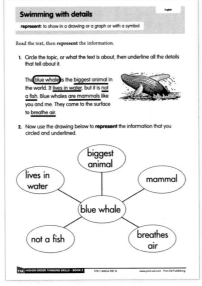

The (blue whale) is the biggest animal in the world. It lives in water, but it is not a fish. Blue whales are mammals like you and me. They come to the surface to breathe air.

2. Now use the drawing below to **represent** the information that you circled and underlined.

```
        biggest
        animal
lives in           mammal
 water
        blue whale
not a fish         breathes
                     air
```

Page 114

Animal coverings

evaluate: to judge carefully

Animals have different body coverings.
Some animals have feathers, hair, scales or a shell.
Look at the animals. Write what kind of covering each animal has.

1.

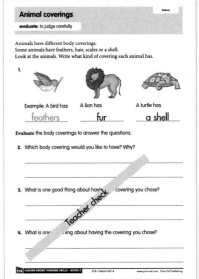

Example: A bird has **feathers** A lion has **fur** A turtle has **a shell**

Evaluate the body coverings to answer the questions.

2. Which body covering would you like to have? Why?

_____

3. What is one good thing about having the covering you chose?

_____

4. What is one ____ thing about having the covering you chose?

_____

Teacher check

Page 118

Meal deal

analyse: to study how parts go together

At the Dingdong Diner, you can order a tasty sandwich, bowl of soup or salad for a great price!

Analyse each row in the chart. Look at what is in the row and the total cost at the end of the row. Rows go across or up and down. Find the cost of each item.
Hint: Start by finding the cost of the sandwich.

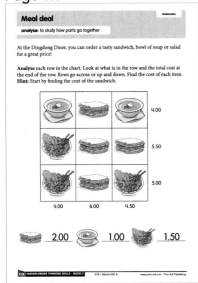

			4.00
			5.50
			5.00
4.00	6.00	4.50	

🥪 **2.00** 🍲 **1.00** 🥗 **1.50**

Page 119

Cool it!

rank: to put in order by value

Oscar lives in Rome. It is very hot there during summer. In fact, it is 41 °C today! Oscar wants to cool off. **Rank** the things Oscar can do to cool off. Write 1, 2, 3 or 4 in the box next to each picture. Use the number 1 for the best thing he can do to cool off.

1. **3** **1**
   2 **4**

Explain your choice for the best way to cool off.

2. _____

Teacher check

Page 121

Up, up and away!

order: to list things in a certain way

Pretend you are a pilot from Perth, Western Australia. Look at the map to see the cities you will fly to.

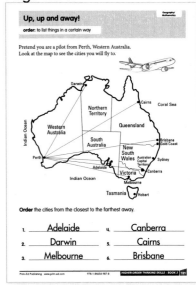

Order the cities from the closest to the farthest away.

1. **Adelaide** 4. **Canberra**
2. **Darwin** 5. **Cairns**
3. **Melbourne** 6. **Brisbane**

Page 123

Clever counting

organise: make something easy to understand or do

Pretend you have seven 50 tokens, seven 20 tokens and seven 10 tokens. Group the tokens so they are easy to add up. Draw a picture showing how you would **organise** the tokens.

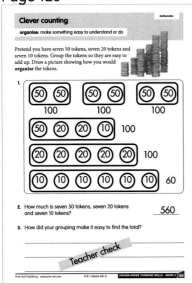

1.
(50) (50) **100** (50) (50) **100** (50) (50) **100**
(50) (20) (20) (10) **100**
(20) (20) (20) (20) (20) **100**
(10) (10) (10) (10) (10) (10) **60**

2. How much is seven 50 tokens, seven 20 tokens and seven 10 tokens? **560**

3. How did your grouping make it easy to find the total?

Teacher check

Page 127

Be an editor!

justify: to give a good reason for something

Read the paragraph. Cross out the sentence that does not belong, then write to **justify** why it does not belong.

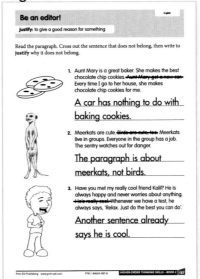

1. Aunt Mary is a great baker. She makes the best chocolate chip cookies. ~~Aunt Mary got a new car.~~ Every time I go to her house, she makes chocolate chip cookies for me.

   A car has nothing to do with baking cookies.

2. Meerkats are cute. ~~Birds are cute, too.~~ Meerkats live in groups. Everyone in the group has a job. The sentry watches out for danger.

   The paragraph is about meerkats, not birds.

3. Have you met my really cool friend Kalil? He is always happy and never worries about anything. ~~He's really cool.~~ Whenever we have a test, he always says, 'Relax. Just do the best you can do'.

   Another sentence already says he is cool.

Page 128

Going home

estimate: to give an idea about the size or value of something

Look at the bear's path to its home. Use the key to **estimate** the length of the path, then answer the question.

Key
1 metre

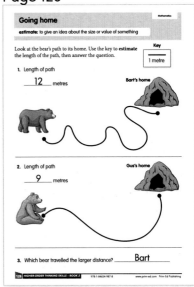

1. Length of path
   12 metres Bart's home

2. Length of path
   9 metres Gus's home

3. Which bear travelled the larger distance? **Bart**

Answers

Page 130

Toy shopping

solve: to find an answer to a problem

Look at the pictures of toys, then answer the questions.

Alison is shopping in New York. She finds some cool toys. Alison has $20.00, so she circles the toy she wants to buy.

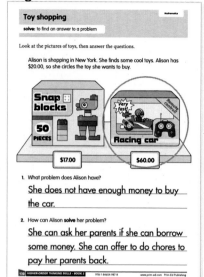

1. What problem does Alison have?

She does not have enough money to buy the car.

2. How can Alison **solve** her problem?

She can ask her parents if she can borrow some money. She can offer to do chores to pay her parents back.

Page 131

In the woods

determine: to work out

Some animals are hiding in the woods. Read the clues to **determine** where they are, then write their names in the correct boxes.

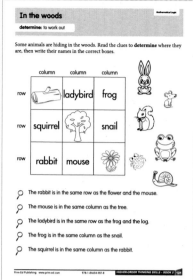

	column	column	column
row		ladybird	frog
row	squirrel		snail
row	rabbit	mouse	

- The rabbit is in the same row as the flower and the mouse.
- The mouse is in the same column as the tree.
- The ladybird is in the same row as the frog and the log.
- The frog is in the same column as the snail.
- The squirrel is in the same column as the rabbit.

Page 133

Sharing stickers

visualise: to imagine how something will look

Suppose you found a sheet of eight stickers. You want to cut the sheet in half to share it with a friend.

First **visualise** four different ways to cut the sheet into two pieces with four stickers on each piece. You can cut only along the lines.

Then use a crayon or marker on the sheets below to draw where you would cut. Colour each half of the sheet in a different colour.

Page 138

Holiday time!

determine: to work out

Sofia was leaving to go on a trip at 5.00 p.m. At 12.00 noon, she still had a lot to do to get ready.

Read how Sofia spent her time getting ready, then **determine** how much time she had left before she had to leave.

- ☑ Sofia had lunch at 12.00. She finished half an hour later.
- ☑ Sofia washed clothes for an hour.
- ☑ Sofia spent an hour and a half packing.
- ☑ It took Sofia 45 minutes to clean the house.
- ☑ It took Sofia 30 minutes to water the garden.
- ☑ Sofia spent a quarter of an hour writing a note for the petsitter.

Work space

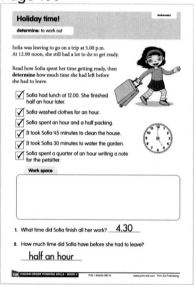

1. What time did Sofia finish all her work? 4.30

2. How much time did Sofia have before she had to leave? half an hour

Page 141

Going shopping!

persuade: to make someone want to do something

Look at Riley's money and the toys. Complete the items.

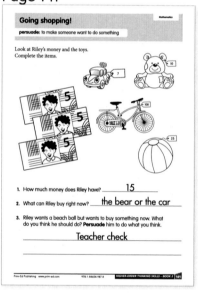

1. How much money does Riley have? 15

2. What can Riley buy right now? the bear or the car

3. Riley wants a beach ball but wants to buy something now. What do you think he should do? **Persuade** him to do what you think.

Teacher check

Page 143

A crawling race

prove: to show that something is true or false

A snail and a caterpillar were racing in the 100-cm crawl. For every 10 cm that the caterpillar travelled, the snail travelled 1 cm.

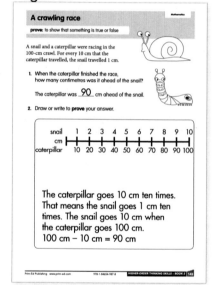

1. When the caterpillar finished the race, how many centimetres was it ahead of the snail?

The caterpillar was 90 cm ahead of the snail.

2. Draw or write to **prove** your answer.

snail	1	2	3	4	5	6	7	8	9	10
cm										
caterpillar	10	20	30	40	50	60	70	80	90	100

The caterpillar goes 10 cm ten times. That means the snail goes 1 cm ten times. The snail goes 10 cm when the caterpillar goes 100 cm.
100 cm – 10 cm = 90 cm